Psalms FOR THE People

EASY CONGREGATIONAL SETTINGS

Compiled by
Norman Warren

Kevin Mayhew

We hope you enjoy *Psalms for the People*. Further copies are available
from your local Kevin Mayhew stockist.

In case of difficulty, or to request a catalogue,
please contact the publisher direct by writing to:

The Sales Department
KEVIN MAYHEW LTD
Buxhall
Stowmarket
Suffolk IP14 3BW

Phone 01449 737978
Fax 01449 737834
E-mail info@kevinmayhewltd.com

First published in Great Britain in 2002 by Kevin Mayhew Ltd.

© Copyright 2002 Kevin Mayhew Ltd.

ISBN 1 84003 883 7
ISMN M 57024 013 5
Catalogue No: 1450242

0 1 2 3 4 5 6 7 8 9

Cover design by Angela Selfe

Music setter: Donald Thomson
Proof reader: Linda Ottewell

Printed and bound in Great Britain

Contents

1, 2, 4, 5, 9, 13, 14, 15, 16, 17, 19, 20, 22, 23, 24, 25, 26, 27, 29, 30, 31, 32, 33, 34, 36, 37, 40, 41, 42, 43, 45, 46, 47, 48, 50, 51, 52, 62, 63, 65, 66, 67, 68, 70, 71, 72, 77, 78, 79, 80, 81, 82, 84, 85, 86, 89, 90, 91, 95, 96, 97, 98, 99, 100, 104, 105, 106, 107, 110, 111, 112, 114, 116, 118, 119:1-8, 119:9-16, 119:33-40, 119:97-104, 119:105-112, 119:129-136, 121, 122, 124, 125, 126, 127, 128, 130, 133, 136, 137, 138, 139, 146, 147, 148, 149, 150.

The list of psalms is not comprehensive and not all verses have been used in some settings. The text makes it clear which verses are included.

Foreword

The Psalms have been probably the single greatest influence on both Hebrew and Christian worship. There is in them an amazing variety of themes and moods, an openness and reality, emotions quickly moving from quiet faith to exuberant praise, from anger with God to calm confidence in him.

Sadly, the singing of Psalms has virtually disappeared from churches and chapels, except for the cathedrals and churches with trained choirs. Metrical Psalms have played an important part in worship – they are included as hymns. There have been many books of Responsorial Psalms, though here the people just sing one verse or part of a verse of a psalm while a cantor or choir sings all the other verses.

Singing Psalms allows a congregation to sing the whole Psalm or at least several verses of it. No cantor or choir is necessary, though they would be an asset. The melody of the chant is simple and easy to remember and changes at the underlined word or part of a word. It can be sung in unison, but in all cases four part harmony has been added. This collection follows the Common Worship Lectionary for Sundays and Principal Feasts. Over 90 Psalms and a number of canticles or other Biblical Psalms are included, but restricted to usually between 6-8 verses.

In the underlining of the words, the aim of this book is to set the ideal against the practical, by using a sensible speech rhythm with the congregation in mind, rather than a trained choir.

NORMAN WARREN

Liturgical Calendar

	YEAR A	YEAR B	YEAR C
ADVENT			
First Sunday of Advent			
Principal Service	Ps 122	Ps 80	Ps 25
Second Sunday of Advent			
Principal Service	Ps 72	Ps 85	Benedictus (p. 22)
Third Sunday of Advent			
Principal Service	Ps 146 or Magnificat (p. 23)	Ps 126 or Magnificat (p. 23)	Song of the Messiah (p.15)
Fourth Sunday of Advent			
Principal Service	Ps 80	Magnificat (p. 23) or Ps 89	Magnificat (p. 23) or Ps 80
CHRISTMAS			
Christmas Eve			
Principal Service	Ps 89	Ps 89	Ps 89
Christmas Day			
Principal Service	Set I: Ps 96	Set II: Ps 97	Set III: Ps 98
First Sunday of Christmas			
Principal Service	Ps 148	Ps 148	Ps 148
Second Sunday of Christmas			
Principal Service	Ps 147	Ps 147	Ps 147
EPIPHANY			
The Epiphany			
Principal Service	Ps 72	Ps 72	Ps 72
The Baptism of Christ (First Sunday of Epiphany)			
Principal Service	Ps 29	Ps 29	Ps 29
Second Sunday of Epiphany			
Principal Service	Ps 40	Ps 139	Ps 36
Third Sunday of Epiphany			
Principal Service	Ps 27	Ps 128	Ps 19
Fourth Sunday of Epiphany			
Principal Service	Ps 36	Ps 111	Ps 48
The Presentation of Christ in the Temple			
Principal Service	Ps 24	Ps 24	Ps 24

ORDINARY TIME

Fifth Sunday before Lent
| Principal Service | Ps 112 | Ps 147 | Ps 138 |

Fourth Sunday before Lent
| Principal Service | Ps 119 | Ps 30 | Ps 1 |

Third Sunday before Lent
| Principal Service | Ps 119 | Ps 41 | Ps 37 |

Second Sunday before Lent
| Principal Service | Ps 136 | Ps 104 | Ps 65 |

Sunday next before Lent
| Principal Service | Ps 2 or 99 | Ps 50 | Ps 99 |

LENT

Ash Wednesday
| Principal Service | Ps 51 | Ps 51 | Ps 51 |

First Sunday of Lent
| Principal Service | Ps 32 | Ps 25 | Ps 91 |

Second Sunday of Lent
| Principal Service | Ps 121 | Ps 22 | Ps 27 |

Third Sunday of Lent
| Principal Service | Ps 95 | Ps 19 | Ps 63 |

Fourth Sunday of Lent
| Principal Service | Ps 23 | Ps 107 | Ps 32 |

Mothering Sunday
| Principal Service | Ps 34 or 127 | Ps 34 or 127 | Ps 34 or 127 |

Fifth Sunday of Lent
| Principal Service | Ps 130 | Ps 51 or 119 | Ps 126 |

Palm Sunday
| Principal Service | Ps 118 or 31 | Ps 118 or 31 | Ps 118 or 31 |

Monday of Holy Week
| Principal Service | Ps 36 | Ps 36 | Ps 36 |

Tuesday of Holy Week
| Principal Service | Ps 71 | Ps 71 | Ps 71 |

Wednesday of Holy Week
| Principal Service | Ps 70 | Ps 70 | Ps 70 |

Maundy Thursday
| Principal Service | Ps 116 | Ps 116 | Ps 116 |

Good Friday
  Principal Service   Ps 22   Ps 22   Ps 22

Easter Eve
(services other than Easter Vigil)
  Principal Service   Ps 31   Ps 31   Ps 31

EASTER

Easter Vigil
                   Ps 136, 46, 16   Ps 136, 46, 16   Ps 136, 46, 16
                   Ps 19,42,43,98   Ps 19,42,43,98   Ps 19,42,43,98
                   Ps 114   Ps 114   Ps 114

Easter Day
  Principal Service   Ps 118   Ps 118   Ps 118

Second Sunday of Easter
  Principal Service   Ps 16   Ps 133   Ps 118 or 150

Third Sunday of Easter
  Principal Service   Ps 116   Ps 4   Ps 30

Fourth Sunday of Easter
  Principal Service   Ps 23   Ps 23   Ps 23

Fifth Sunday of Easter
  Principal Service   Ps 31   Ps 22   Ps 148

Sixth Sunday of Easter
  Principal Service   Ps 66   Ps 98   Ps 67

Ascension Day
  Principal Service   Ps 47   Ps 47   Ps 47

Seventh Sunday of Easter
  Principal Service   Ps 68   Ps 1   Ps 97

Day of Pentecost
  Principal Service   Ps 104   Ps 104   Ps 104

ORDINARY TIME

Trinity Sunday
  Principal Service   Ps 29   Ps 29   Ps 29

Corpus Christi
  Principal Service   Ps 116   Ps 110   Ps 111

Trinity 1
  Principal Service   Ps 46   Ps 139   Ps 96

Trinity 2
  Principal Service   Ps 33   Ps 138   Ps 146

Trinity 3
Principal Service	Ps 116	Ps 20	Ps 5

Trinity 4
Principal Service	Ps 86	Ps 9 or 133	Ps 42, 43

Trinity 5
Principal Service	Ps 13	Ps 130	Ps 77

Trinity 6
Principal Service	Ps 45	Ps 48	Ps 30

Trinity 7
Principal Service	Ps 119	Ps 24	Ps 82

Trinity 8
Principal Service	Ps 139	Ps 89	Ps 52

Trinity 9
Principal Service	Ps 105 or 128	Ps 14	Ps 85

Trinity 10
Principal Service	Ps 17	Ps 51	Ps 107

Trinity 11
Principal Service	Ps 105	Ps 130	Ps 50

Trinity 12
Principal Service	Ps 133	Ps 111	Ps 80

Trinity 13
Principal Service	Ps 124	Ps 84	Ps 71

Trinity 14
Principal Service	Ps 105	Ps 45	Ps 81

Trinity 15
Principal Service	Ps 149	Ps 125	Ps 139

Trinity 16
Principal Service	Ps 114	Ps 19	Ps 14

Trinity 17
Principal Service	Ps 105	Ps 1	Ps 79

Trinity 18
Principal Service	Ps 78	Ps 124	Ps 91

Trinity 19
Principal Service	Ps 19	Ps 26	Ps 137

Trinity 20
Principal Service	Ps 106	Ps 22	Ps 66

Trinity 21
Principal Service	Ps 99	Ps 104	Ps 119

Trinity 22
Principal Service	Ps 90	Ps 34	Ps 65

Bible Sunday
Principal Service	Ps 119: 9-16	Ps 119:33-40	Ps 119:97-104

Dedication Festival
Principal Service	Ps 122 or 24	Ps 122 or 24	Ps 122 or 24

All Saints' Day
Principal Service	Ps 34	Ps 24	Ps 149

All Saints' Day
(on 1 November if the above is used on the Sunday)
Principal Service	Ps 33	Ps 33	Ps 33

Fourth Sunday before Advent
Principal Service	Ps 43	Ps 119	Ps 32

Third Sunday before Advent
Principal Service	Song of the Wilderness (p.14)	Ps 62 or Ps 70	Ps 17

Second Sunday before Advent
Principal Service	Ps 90	Ps 16	Ps 98

Christ the King
Principal Service	Ps 95	Ps 99	Ps 46

A Song of the Wilderness

Geoffrey Weaver

(Advent)

1 The wilderness and the dry land shall re-<u>joice</u>, ♦
   the desert shall blossom and <u>burst</u> into song.

2 They shall see the glory of the <u>Lord</u>, ♦
   the majesty <u>of</u> our God.

3 Strengthen the weary <u>hands</u>, ♦
   and make firm the <u>fee</u>ble knees.

4 Say to the anxious, 'Be strong, fear not:
   your God is coming with <u>judge</u>ment, ♦
   coming with <u>judgement</u> to save you.'

5 Then shall the eyes of the blind be <u>o</u>pened, ♦
   and the ears of the <u>deaf</u> unstopped;

6 Then shall the lame leap like a <u>hart</u>, ♦
   and the tongue of the dumb <u>sing</u> for joy.

7 For waters shall break forth in the <u>wilde</u>rness, ♦
   and <u>streams in</u> the desert;

8 The ransomed of the Lord shall return with <u>singing</u>, ♦
   with everlasting <u>joy upon</u> their heads.

9 Joy and gladness shall be <u>theirs</u>, ♦
   and sorrow and sighing shall <u>flee</u> away.

Isaiah 35: 1, 2b-4a, 4c-6, 10

   Glory be to the Father and to the <u>Son</u>; ♦
   and to the <u>Ho</u>ly Spirit;
   as it was in the beginning is <u>now</u> ♦
   and shall be for <u>ever</u>. Amen.

A Song of the Messiah — *(Christmas)*

David Wilson

1 The people who walked in darkness have seen a <u>great</u> light; ♦
   those who dwelt in a land of deep darkness:
     upon them the <u>light</u> has dawned.

2 You have increased their joy and given them great <u>glad</u>ness; ♦
   they rejoiced before you as with <u>joy at</u> the harvest.

3 For you have shattered the yoke that <u>burdened</u> them; ♦
   the collar that lay heavy <u>on</u> their shoulders.

4 For to us a child is born and to us a son <u>is</u> given, ♦
   and the government shall be up-<u>on</u> his shoulder.

5 And his name will be called: Wonderful Counsellor:
     the <u>Mighty</u> God; ♦
   the Everlasting Father: the <u>Prince</u> of Peace.

6 Of the increase of his government <u>and of</u> peace ♦
   there <u>will be</u> no end.

7 Upon the throne of David and over his <u>kingdom</u>, ♦
   to establish and uphold it with <u>justice</u> and righteousness.

8 From this time forth and for <u>evermore</u>; ♦
   the zeal of the Lord of <u>hosts</u> will do this.

Isaiah 9:2, 3b, 4a, 6, 7

Glory be to the Father and to the <u>Son</u>; ♦
and to the <u>Holy</u> Spirit;
as it was in the beginning is <u>now</u> ♦
and shall be for <u>ever</u>. Amen.

A Song of Redemption   *(Christmas)*

Geoffrey Weaver

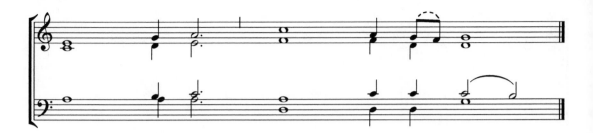

1   The Father has delivered us from the dominion of <u>dark</u>ness, ♦
    and transferred us to the kingdom of <u>his be</u>loved Son;

2   In whom we have re<u>demp</u>tion, ♦
    the forgiveness <u>of</u> our sins.

3   He is the image of the invisible <u>God</u>, ♦
    the firstborn of <u>all</u> creation.

4   For in him all things were cre<u>at</u>ed, ♦
    in heaven and on earth, visible <u>and</u> invisible.

5   All things were created through him and <u>for</u> him, ♦
    he is before all things and in him all things <u>hold</u> together.

6   He is the head of the body, the <u>Church</u>, ♦
    he is the beginning, the firstborn <u>from</u> the dead.

7   In him all the fullness of God was pleased to <u>dwell</u>; ♦
    and through him God was pleased to <u>reconcile</u> all things.

Colossians 1: 13-18a, 19, 20a

    Glory be to the Father and to the <u>Son</u>; ♦
    and to the <u>Holy</u> Spirit;
    as it was in the beginning is <u>now</u> ♦
    and shall be for <u>ever</u>. Amen.

A Song of the New Jerusalem   *(Epiphany)*

Geoffrey Weaver

1   Arise, shine out, for your light <u>has</u> come, ♦
    the glory of the Lord is <u>rising</u> upon you.

2   Though night still covers <u>the</u> earth, ♦
    and <u>darkness</u> the peoples;

3   Above you the Holy One <u>a</u>-rises, ♦
    and above you God's <u>glory</u> appears.

4   The nations will come to <u>your</u> light, ♦
    and kings to your <u>dawn</u>ing brightness.

5   Your gates will lie <u>open con</u>-tinually, ♦
    shut neither by day <u>nor</u> by night.

6   The sound of violence shall be heard no longer in <u>your</u> land, ♦
    or ruin and devastation with<u>in</u> your borders.

7   You will call your walls, Sal<u>va</u>tion, ♦
    and your <u>gates</u>, Praise.

8   No more will the sun give you <u>day</u>light, ♦
    nor moonlight <u>shine up</u>-on you;

9   But the Lord will be your everlas<u>ting</u> light, ♦
    your God will <u>be</u> your splendour.

10   For you shall be called the city <u>of</u> God, ♦
    the dwelling of the <u>Holy</u> One of Israel.

Isaiah 60: 1-3, 11a 18, 19, 14b

    Glory be to the Father and to the <u>Son</u>; ♦
    and to the <u>Holy</u> Spirit;
    as it was in the beginning is <u>now</u> ♦
    and shall be for <u>ever</u>. Amen.

A Song of Praise (Glory and Honour) *(Epiphany)*

Norman Warren

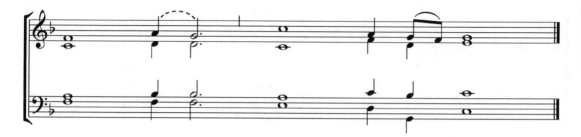

1 You are worthy, our Lord and <u>God</u>, ♦
   to receive glory and <u>honour</u> and power.

2 For you have created <u>all</u> things, ♦
   and by your will they <u>have</u> their being.

3 You are worthy, O Lamb, for you were <u>slain</u>, ♦
   and by your blood you ransomed for God:
      saints from every tribe and <u>language</u> and nation.

4 You have made them to be a kingdom and priests
      serving our <u>God</u>, ♦
   and they will reign with <u>you</u> on earth.

Revelation 4: 11; 5: 9b, 10

   To the One who sits on the throne and to the <u>Lamb</u> ♦
   be blessing and honour, glory and might:
      for ever and <u>ever</u>. Amen.

A Song of Christ the Servant (Lent)

Geoffrey Weaver

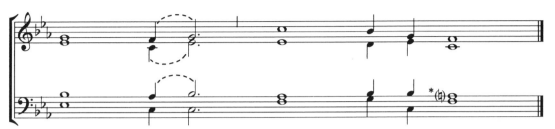

* Tenors sing A♮ last time only.

1 Christ suffered for you, leaving you an ex<u>am</u>ple, ♦
  that you should follow <u>in</u> his steps.

2 He committed no sin, no guile was found on his <u>lips</u>, ♦
  when he was reviled, he did not re<u>vile</u> in turn.

3 When he suffered, he did not <u>threat</u>en, ♦
  but he trusted himself to God who <u>judg</u>-es justly.

4 Christ himself bore our sins in his body on the <u>tree</u>, ♦
  that we might die to sin and <u>live</u> to righteousness.

5 By his wounds, you have been healed:
    for you were straying like <u>sheep</u>. ♦
  but have now returned
    to the shepherd and guardian <u>of</u> your souls.

1 Peter 2: 21b-25

  Glory be to the Father and to the <u>Son</u>; ♦
  and to the <u>Ho</u>ly Spirit;
  as it was in the beginning is <u>now</u> ♦
  and shall be for <u>ev</u>er. Amen.

19

The Easter Anthems

Norman Warren

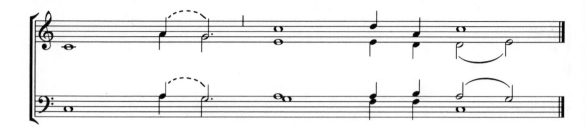

1 Christ our passover has been sacrificed for <u>us</u>: ♦
   so let us <u>celebrate</u> the feast,

2 not with the old leaven of corruption and <u>wicked</u>ness: ♦
   but with the unleavened bread of sin-<u>cerity</u> and truth.

1 Corinthians 5:7b, 8

3 Christ once raised from the dead dies no <u>more</u>: ♦
   death has no more dominion <u>o</u>-ver him.

4 In dying he died to sin once for <u>all</u>: ♦
   in living he <u>lives</u> to God.

5 See yourselves therefore as dead to <u>sin</u>: ♦
   and alive to God in Jesus <u>Christ</u> our Lord.

Romans 6:9-11

6 Christ has been raised from the <u>dead</u>: ♦
   the first fruits of <u>those</u> who sleep.

7 For as by man came <u>death</u>: ♦
   by man has come also the resurrection <u>of</u> the dead;

8 for as in Adam all <u>die</u>: ♦
   even so in Christ shall all be <u>made</u> alive.

1 Corinthians 15:20-22

   Glory be to the Father and to the <u>Son</u>; ♦
   and to the <u>Holy</u> Spirit;
   as it was in the beginning is <u>now</u> ♦
   and shall be for <u>ever</u>. Amen.

A Song of Ezekiel

(Pentecost)

Norman Warren

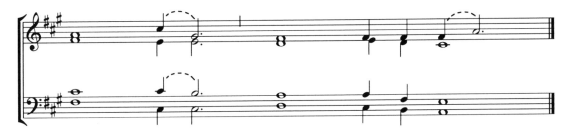

1 I will take you from the <u>na</u>tions, ♦
   and gather you from <u>all</u> the countries.

2 I will sprinkle clean water up<u>on</u> you, ♦
   and you shall be clean from <u>all your</u> uncleannesses.

3 A new heart I <u>will give</u> you, ♦
   and put a new <u>spirit</u> within you.

4 And I will remove from your body the heart of <u>stone</u> ♦
   and give you a <u>heart</u> of flesh.

5 You shall be my <u>peo</u>-ple, ♦
   and I will <u>be</u> your God.

Ezekiel 36:24-26, 28b

   Glory be to the Father and to the <u>Son</u>; ♦
   and to the <u>Holy</u> Spirit;
   as it was in the beginning is <u>now</u> ♦
   and shall be for <u>ever</u>. Amen.

Benedictus

(The Song of Zechariah)

Geoffrey Weaver

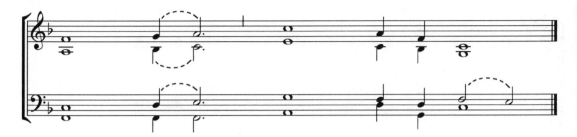

1 Blessed be the Lord the God of Is-rael, ♦
   who has come to his people and set them free.

2 He has raised up for us a mighty Sa-viour, ♦
   born of the house of his servant David.

3 Through his holy prophets God promised of old ♦
   to save us from our enemies:
     from the hands of all that hate us,

4 To show mercy to our ancestors, ♦
   and to remember his ho-ly covenant.

5 This was the oath God swore to our father Abra-ham: ♦
   to set us free from the hands of our enemies,

6 Free to worship him without fear, ♦
   holy and righteous in his sight:
     all the days of our life.

7 And you, child, shall be called the prophet of the Most High, ♦
   for you will go before the Lord to prepare his way,

8 To give his people knowledge of salvation, ♦
   by the forgiveness of all their sins.

9 In the tender compassion of our God, ♦
   the dawn from on high shall break upon us,

10 To shine on those who dwell in darkness and the shadow of death, ♦
    and to guide our feet into the way of peace.

Luke 1:68-79

   Glory be to the Father and to the Son; ♦
   and to the Holy Spirit;
   as it was in the beginning is now ♦
   and shall be for ever. Amen.

Magnificat

(The Song of Mary)

Norman Warren

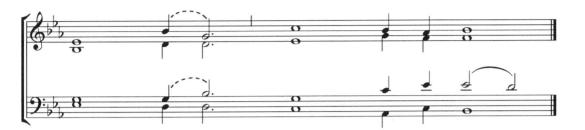

1 My soul proclaims the greatness of the Lord:
    my spirit rejoices in God my <u>Sa</u>-viour: ♦
he has looked with favour on his <u>low</u>-ly servant.

2 From this day all generations will call me <u>bless</u>-ed; ♦
the Almighty has done great things for me
    and holy <u>is</u> his name.

3 He has mercy on those who <u>fear</u> him, ♦
from generation to <u>gen</u>eration.

4 He has shown strength with his <u>arm</u> ♦
and has scattered the proud in <u>their</u> conceit,

5 Casting down the mighty from their <u>thrones</u> ♦
and lifting <u>up</u> the lowly.

6 He has filled the hungry with <u>good</u> things ♦
and sent the <u>rich a</u>-way empty.

7 He has come to the aid of his servant <u>Is</u>-rael, ♦
to remember his <u>prom</u>ise of mercy,

8 The promise made to our <u>an</u>-cestors, ♦
to Abraham and his <u>children</u> for ever.

Luke 1:46-55

Glory be to the Father and to the <u>Son</u>; ♦
and to the <u>Ho</u>ly Spirit;
as it was in the beginning is <u>now</u> ♦
and shall be for <u>ever</u>. Amen.

Nunc dimittis
(The Song of Simeon)

Norman Warren

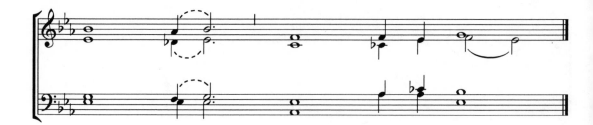

1 Now, Lord, you let your servant go in <u>peace</u>: ♦
your word has <u>been</u> fulfilled.

2 My own eyes have seen the sal<u>va</u>tion ♦
which you have prepared in the sight of <u>ev</u>-ery people;

3 A light to reveal you to the <u>na</u>tions ♦
and the glory of your <u>peo</u>-ple Israel.

Luke 2:29-32

Glory be to the Father and to the <u>Son</u>; ♦
and to the <u>Ho</u>ly Spirit;
as it was in the beginning is <u>now</u> ♦
and shall be for <u>ever</u>. Amen.

Benedicite

(A Song of Creation)

Norman Warren

1 Bless the Lord all you works of the <u>Lord</u>: ♦
sing his praise and <u>ex-alt him</u> for ever.

2 Bless the Lord you <u>heavens</u>: ♦
sing his praise and <u>ex-alt him</u> for ever.

3 Bless the Lord you angels of the <u>Lord</u>: ♦
sing his praise and <u>ex-alt him</u> for ever.

4 Bless the Lord all people on <u>earth</u>: ♦
sing his praise and <u>ex-alt him</u> for ever.

5 O people of God bless the <u>Lord</u>: ♦
sing his praise and <u>ex-alt him</u> for ever.

6 Bless the Lord you priests of the <u>Lord</u>: ♦
sing his praise and <u>ex-alt him</u> for ever.

7 Bless the Lord you servants of the <u>Lord</u>: ♦
sing his praise and <u>ex-alt him</u> for ever.

8 Bless the Lord all you of upright <u>spi</u>-rit: ♦
bless the Lord you that are holy and <u>humble</u> in heart;

9 Bless the Father, the Son and the Holy <u>Spi</u>-rit: ♦
sing his praise and <u>ex-alt him</u> for ever.

A Song of the Lamb

(Ordinary Time)

Norman Warren

1 Salvation and glory and power belong to our <u>God</u>, ♦
   whose judgements are <u>true</u> and just.

2 Praise our God, all you his <u>servants</u>, ♦
   all who fear him, both <u>small</u> and great.

3 The Lord our God, the Almighty, <u>reigns</u>: ♦
   let us rejoice and exult and give <u>him</u> the glory.

4 For the marriage of the Lamb has <u>come</u> ♦
   and his bride has <u>made her</u>self ready.

5 Blessed are those who are in-<u>vited</u> ♦
   to the wedding banquet <u>of</u> the Lamb.

Revelation 19:1b, 5b, 6b, 7, 9b

   To the One who sits on the throne and to the <u>Lamb</u> ♦
   be blessing and honour, glory and might:
       for ever and <u>ever</u>. Amen.

The Song of Christ's Glory

Norman Warren

1 Christ Jesus was in the form of <u>God</u>, ♦
   but he did not cling to e-<u>quality</u> with God.

2 He emptied himself, taking the form of a <u>ser</u>-vant, ♦
   and was born in our <u>human</u> likeness.

3 Being found in human form he <u>humbled himself</u>, ♦
   and became obedient unto death, even <u>death on</u> a cross.

4 Therefore God has highly ex-<u>alted</u> him, ♦
   and bestowed on him the name above <u>ev</u>-ery name,

5 That at the name of Jesus, every knee should <u>bow</u>, ♦
   in heaven and on earth and <u>under</u> the earth;

6 And every tongue confess that Jesus Christ is <u>Lord</u>, ♦
   to the glory of <u>God</u> the Father.

Philippians 2:5-11

   Glory be to the Father and to the <u>Son</u>; ♦
   and to the <u>Holy</u> Spirit;
   as it was in the beginning is <u>now</u> ♦
   and shall be for <u>ever</u>. Amen.

Great and Wonderful

Norman Warren

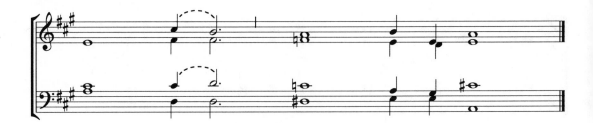

1 Great and wonderful are your <u>deeds</u>, ♦
   Lord <u>God the</u> Almighty.

2 Just and true are your <u>ways</u>, ♦
   O <u>ruler of</u> the nations.

3 Who shall not revere and praise your name, O <u>Lord</u>? ♦
   for you a-<u>lone</u> are holy.

4 All nations shall come and worship in your <u>pre</u>-sence: ♦
   for your just dealings have <u>been</u> revealed.

Revelation 15:3, 4

   To the One who sits on the throne and to the <u>Lamb</u> ♦
   be blessing and honour, glory and might:
      for ever and <u>ever</u>. Amen.

Bless the Lord

(The Song of the Three)

Geoffrey Weaver

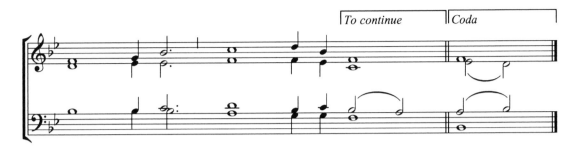

1 Blessed are you, the God of our <u>an</u>cestors, ♦
worthy to be praised and ex-<u>alted</u> for ever.

2 Blessed is your holy and glor<u>ious</u> name, ♦
worthy to be praised and ex-<u>alted</u> for ever.

3 Blessed are you, in your holy and glor<u>ious</u> temple, ♦
worthy to be praised and ex-<u>alted</u> for ever.

4 Blessed are you who look into <u>the</u> depths, ♦
worthy to be praised and ex-<u>alted</u> for ever.

5 Blessed are you, enthroned on the <u>cheru</u>bim, ♦
worthy to be praised and ex-<u>alted</u> for ever.

6 Blessed are you on the throne of <u>your</u> kingdom, ♦
worthy to be praised and ex-<u>alted</u> for ever.

7 Blessed are you in the heights <u>of</u> heaven, ♦
worthy to be praised and ex-<u>alted</u> for ever.

The Song of the Three 29-34

Bless the Father, the Son and the Ho<u>ly</u> Spirit, ♦
worthy to be praised and ex-<u>alted</u> for ever.

Saviour of the World

Norman Warren

1 Jesus, Saviour of the world, come to us in your <u>mercy</u>: ♦
   we look to you to <u>save</u> and help us.

2 By your cross and your life laid down, you set your people <u>free</u>: ♦
   we look to you to <u>save</u> and help us.

3 When they were ready to perish, you saved your di-<u>sciples</u>: ♦
   we look to you to <u>come to</u> our help.

4 In the greatness of your mercy, loose us from our <u>chains,</u> ♦
   forgive the sins of <u>all</u> your people.

5 Make yourself known as our Saviour and mighty de-<u>liverer</u>; ♦
   save and help us that <u>we</u> may praise you.

6 Come now and dwell with us, Lord Christ <u>Jesus</u>: ♦
   hear our prayer and be <u>with</u> us always.

7 And when you come in your <u>glory</u>: ♦
   make us to be one with you: and to share the <u>life of</u> your kingdom.

Psalm 1

Norman Warren

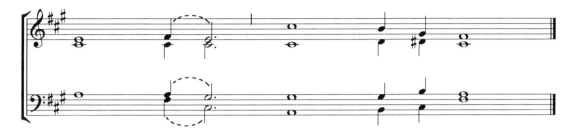

1 Blessed are they who have not walked
   in the counsel of the <u>wick</u>ed, ♦
   nor lingered in the way of sinners,
      nor sat in the assembly <u>of</u> the scornful.

2 Their delight is in the law of the <u>Lord</u> ♦
   and they meditate on his law <u>day</u> and night.

3 Like a tree planted by streams of water:
      bearing fruit in due season, with leaves that do not <u>wi</u>ther, ♦
   whatever they do, <u>it</u> shall prosper.

4 As for the wicked, it is not so with <u>them</u>; ♦
   they are like chaff which the wind <u>blows</u> away.

5 Therefore the wicked shall not be able to stand in the <u>judge</u>ment, ♦
   nor the sinner in the congregation <u>of</u> the righteous.

6 For the Lord knows the way of the <u>righ</u>teous, ♦
   but the way of the <u>wicked</u> shall perish.

   Glory be to the Father and to the <u>Son</u>; ♦
   and to the <u>Ho</u>ly Spirit;
   as it was in the beginning is <u>now</u> ♦
   and shall be for <u>ever</u>. Amen.

Psalm 2

Barry Ferguson

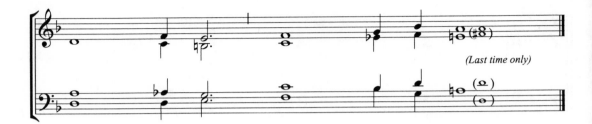

(Last time only)

1 Why are the nations in <u>tu</u>mult, ♦
  and why do the peoples de<u>vise a</u> vain plot?

2 The kings of the earth rise up:
    and the rulers take counsel to<u>ge</u>ther, ♦
  against the Lord and a<u>gainst his</u> anointed:

3 'Let us break their bonds a-<u>sun</u>der ♦
  and cast away their <u>cords</u> from us.'

4 He who dwells in heaven shall laugh them <u>to</u> scorn; ♦
  the Lord shall have them <u>in</u> derision.

5 Then shall he speak to them in <u>his</u> wrath ♦
  and terrify them <u>in</u> his fury:

6 'Yet have I set <u>my</u> king ♦
  upon my holy <u>hill</u> of Zion.'

11 Serve the Lord with fear, and with trembling kiss <u>his</u> feet, ♦
  lest he be angry and you perish from the way,
    for his wrath is <u>quick</u>-ly kindled.

12 Happy are <u>all</u> they ♦
  who take <u>refuge</u> in him.

  Glory be to the Father and to the <u>Son</u>; ♦
  and to the <u>Ho</u>ly Spirit;
  as it was in the beginning is <u>now</u> ♦
  and shall be for <u>ever</u>. Amen.

Psalm 4

Peter White

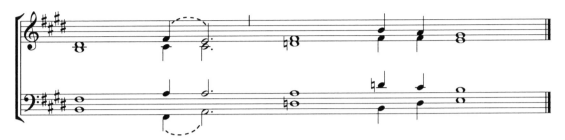

1 Answer me when I call, O God of my <u>righteous</u>ness; ♦
   you set me at liberty when I was in trouble;
      have mercy on me and <u>hear</u> my prayer.

2 How long will you nobles dishonour my <u>glory</u>; ♦
   how long will you love vain things and seek <u>a</u>-fter falsehood?

3 But know that the Lord has shown me his marvellous <u>kind</u>ness; ♦
   when I call upon the Lord, <u>he</u> will hear me.

4 Stand in awe, and <u>sin</u> not; ♦
   commune with your own heart upon your bed, <u>and</u> be still.

5 Offer the sacrifices of <u>righteous</u>ness ♦
   and put your <u>trust in</u> the Lord.

6 There are many that say, 'Who will show us any <u>good</u>?' ♦
   Lord, lift up the light of your <u>countenance</u> upon us.

7 You have put gladness in my <u>heart</u>, ♦
   more than when their corn and wine and <u>oil</u> increase.

8 In peace I will lie down and <u>sleep</u>, ♦
   for it is you Lord, only, who make me <u>dwell</u> in safety.

   Glory be to the Father and to the <u>Son</u>; ♦
   and to the <u>Holy</u> Spirit;
   as it was in the beginning is <u>now</u> ♦
   and shall be for <u>ever</u>. Amen.

Psalm 5

Norman Warren

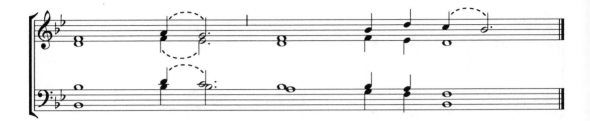

1 Give ear to my words, O <u>Lord</u>; ♦
consider my <u>la</u>mentation.

2 Hearken to the voice of my crying, my King and my <u>God</u>, ♦
for to you I <u>make</u> my prayer.

3 In the morning, Lord, you will hear my <u>voice</u>; ♦
early in the morning I make my appeal to <u>you, and</u> look up.

4 For you are the God who takes no pleasure in <u>wicked</u>ness; ♦
no evil can <u>dwell</u> with you.

7 But as for me, through the greatness of your mercy,
   I will come into your <u>house</u>; ♦
I will bow down towards your holy temple in <u>awe</u> of you.

8 Lead me, Lord, in your righteousness,
   because of my e<u>nem</u>-ies; ♦
make your way straight be<u>fore</u> my face.

   Glory be to the Father and to the <u>Son</u>; ♦
   and to the <u>Ho</u>ly Spirit;
   as it was in the beginning is <u>now</u> ♦
   and shall be for <u>ever</u>. Amen.

Psalm 9

John Barnard

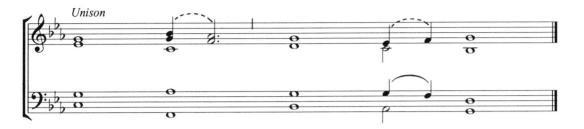

1 I will give thanks to you, Lord, with my whole <u>heart</u>; ♦
   I will tell of all your <u>marvel</u>lous works.

2 I will be glad and rejoice in <u>you</u>; ♦
   I will make music to your name, <u>O</u> Most High.

6 The enemy was utterly laid <u>waste</u>. ♦
   You uprooted their cities;
     their very <u>memory</u> has perished.

7 But the Lord shall endure for <u>e</u>-ver; ♦
   he has made fast his <u>throne</u> for judgement.

8 For he shall rule the world with <u>righteous</u>ness ♦
   and govern the <u>peoples</u> with equity.

9 Then will the Lord be a refuge for the op<u>pressed</u>, ♦
   a refuge in the <u>time</u> of trouble.

10 And those who know your name will put their trust in <u>you</u>, ♦
   for you, Lord, have never failed <u>those</u> who seek you.

   Glory be to the Father and to the <u>Son</u>; ♦
   and to the <u>Ho</u>ly Spirit;
   as it was in the beginning is <u>now</u> ♦
   and shall be for <u>ever</u>. Amen.

Psalm 13

Barry Ferguson

Chant A

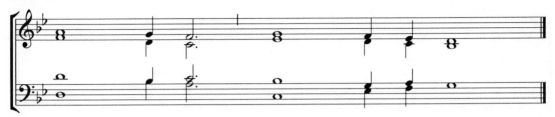

Chant B

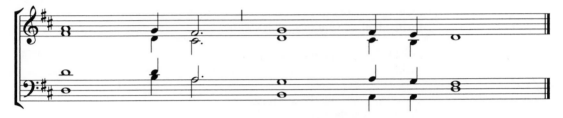

A 1 How long will you forget me, O Lord; for <u>ever</u>? ♦
    How long will you hide your <u>face</u> from me?

 2 How long shall I have anguish in my soul:
    and grief in my heart, day after <u>day</u>? ♦
    How long shall my enemy triumph <u>over</u> me?

 3 Look upon me and answer, O Lord my <u>God</u>; ♦
    lighten my eyes, lest I <u>sleep</u> in death;

 4 Lest my enemy say, 'I have prevailed a-<u>gainst</u> him,' ♦
    and my foes rejoice that <u>I</u> have fallen.

B 5 But I put my trust in your steadfast <u>love</u>; ♦
    my heart will rejoice in <u>your</u> salvation.

 6 I will sing to the <u>Lord</u>, ♦
    for he has dealt so <u>bountifully</u> with me.

    Glory be to the Father and to the <u>Son</u>; ♦
    and to the <u>Holy</u> Spirit;
    as it was in the beginning is <u>now</u> ♦
    and shall be for <u>ever</u>. Amen.

Alternative setting
John Barnard

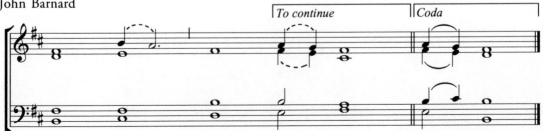

Psalm 14

Peter White

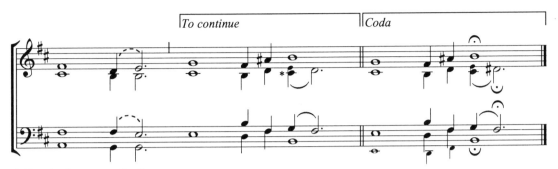

* Cue sized notes are for Organ

1 The fool has said in his heart, 'There is no <u>God</u>.' ♦
Corrupt are they, and abominable in their wickedness;
    there is no one <u>that</u> does good.

2 The Lord has looked down from heaven
    upon the children of <u>earth</u>, ♦
to see if there is anyone who is wise
    and <u>seeks</u> after God.

3 But every one has turned back;
    all alike have become co<u>rrupt</u>: ♦
there is none that does good; <u>no</u>, not one.

4 Have they no knowledge, those evil<u>do</u>-ers, ♦
who eat up my people as if they ate bread
    and do not call up<u>on</u> the Lord?

5 There shall they be in great <u>fear</u>; ♦
for God is in the company <u>of</u> the righteous.

6 Though they would confound the counsel of the <u>poor</u>, ♦
yet the Lord shall <u>be</u> their refuge.

7 O that Israel's salvation would come out of <u>Zi</u>-on! ♦
When the Lord restores the fortunes of his people,
    then will Jacob rejoice and <u>Israel</u> be glad.

Glory be to the Father and to the <u>Son</u>; ♦
and to the <u>Holy</u> Spirit;
as it was in the beginning is <u>now</u> ♦
and shall be for <u>ever</u>. Amen.

Psalm 15

Norman Warren

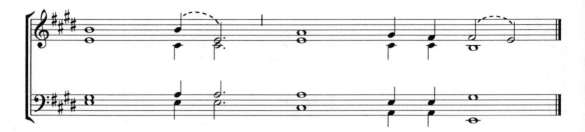

1 Lord, who may dwell in your <u>taber</u>nacle? ♦
  Who may rest upon your <u>ho</u>ly hill?

2 Whoever leads an uncorrupt <u>life</u> ♦
  and does the <u>thing that</u> is right;

3 Who speaks the truth from the <u>heart</u> ♦
  and bears no deceit <u>on</u> the tongue;

4 Who does no evil to a <u>friend</u> ♦
  and pours no <u>scorn on</u> a neighbour;

5 In whose sight the wicked are not es-<u>teemed,</u> ♦
  but who honours those who <u>fear</u> the Lord.

6 Whoever has sworn to a <u>neigh</u>bour ♦
  and never goes back <u>on</u> that word;

7 Who does not lend money in hope of <u>gain,</u> ♦
  nor takes a bribe a-<u>gainst</u> the innocent;

8 Whoever does these <u>things</u> ♦
  shall <u>nev</u>er fall.

  Glory be to the Father and to the <u>Son;</u> ♦
  and to the <u>Ho</u>ly Spirit;
  as it was in the beginning is <u>now</u> ♦
  and shall be for <u>ev</u>er. Amen.

Psalm 16

John Barnard

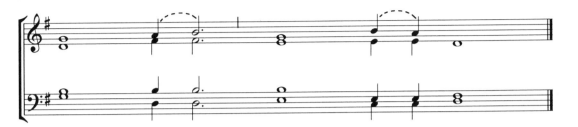

1 Preserve me, O God, for in you have I taken <u>ref</u>uge; ♦
   I have said to the Lord, 'You are my lord,
     all my good de-<u>pends</u> on you.'

2 All my delight is upon the godly that are in the <u>land</u>, ♦
   upon those who are <u>nob</u>le in heart.

4 The Lord himself is my portion and my <u>cup</u>; ♦
   in your hands alone <u>is</u> my fortune.

5 My share has fallen in a <u>fair</u> land; ♦
   indeed, I have a <u>good</u>ly heritage.

6 I will bless the Lord who has given me <u>coun</u>sel, ♦
   and in the night watches he in-<u>structs</u> my heart.

7 I have set the Lord always be-<u>fore</u> me; ♦
   he is at my right hand; I <u>shall</u> not fall.

8 Wherefore my heart is glad and my spirit re-<u>joices</u>; ♦
   my flesh also shall <u>rest</u> secure.

9 For you will not abandon my soul to <u>Death</u>, ♦
   nor suffer your faithful one to <u>see</u> the Pit.

10 You will show me the path of life; ♦
     in your presence is the fullness of <u>joy</u> ♦
   and in your right hand are pleasures for <u>e</u>-vermore.

   Glory be to the Father and to the <u>Son</u>; ♦
   and to the <u>Ho</u>ly Spirit;
   as it was in the beginning is <u>now</u> ♦
   and shall be for <u>ev</u>er. Amen.

Psalm 17

Barry Ferguson

1 Hear my just cause, O Lord; consider my <u>com</u>-plaint; ♦
 listen to my prayer, which comes not from <u>ly</u>-ing lips.

2 Let my vindication come forth from <u>your</u> presence; ♦
 let your eyes behold <u>what</u> is right.

3 Weigh my heart, examine me <u>by</u> night, ♦
 refine me, and you will find no im-<u>purity</u> in me.

4 My mouth does not trespass for earthly <u>re</u>-wards; ♦
 I have heeded the <u>words of</u> your lips.

5 My footsteps hold fast in the ways of your <u>commandments</u>; ♦
 my feet have not stumbled <u>in</u> your paths.

6 I call upon you, O God, for you <u>will</u> answer me; ♦
 incline your ear to me, and listen <u>to</u> my words.

7 Show me your marvellous <u>loving</u>-kindness, ♦
 O Saviour of those who take refuge at your right hand
  from those who <u>rise up</u> against them.

8 Keep me as the apple of <u>your</u> eye; ♦
 hide me under the shadow <u>of</u> your wings.

 Glory be to the Father and to the <u>Son</u>; ♦
 and to the <u>Holy</u> Spirit;
 as it was in the beginning is <u>now</u> ♦
 and shall be for <u>ever</u>. Amen.

Psalm 19

Peter White

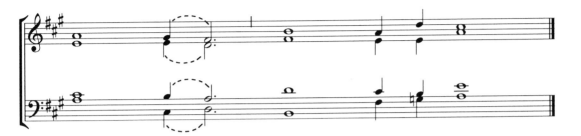

1 The heavens are telling the glory of <u>God</u> ♦
and the firmament pro<u>claims</u> his handiwork.

2 One day pours out its song to an<u>other</u> ♦
and one night unfolds knowledge to an-<u>other</u>.

3 They have neither speech nor <u>language</u> ♦
and their voices <u>are</u> not heard,

4 Yet their sound has gone out into all <u>lands</u> ♦
and their words to the <u>ends of</u> the world.

7 The law of the Lord is perfect, reviving the <u>soul</u>; ♦
the testimony of the Lord is sure:
and gives wisdom <u>to</u> the simple.

12 Who can tell how often they <u>o</u>-ffend? ♦
O cleanse me from my <u>sec</u>ret faults!

13 Keep your servant also from presumptuous sins:
lest they get dominion <u>over</u> me; ♦
so shall I be undefiled:
and innocent of <u>great</u> offence.

14 Let the words of my mouth and the meditation of my heart
be acceptable in your <u>sight</u>, ♦
O Lord, my strength and <u>my</u> redeemer.

Glory be to the Father and to the <u>Son</u>; ♦
and to the <u>Holy</u> Spirit;
as it was in the beginning is <u>now</u> ♦
and shall be for <u>ever</u>. Amen.

Psalm 20

Norman Warren

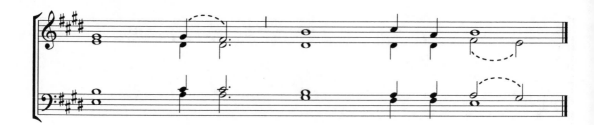

1 May the Lord hear you in the day of <u>trou</u>ble, ♦
the name of the God of <u>Jacob</u> defend you;

2 Send you help from <u>his</u> sanctuary ♦
and strengthen you <u>out</u> of Zion;

3 Remember all your <u>offerings</u> ♦
and accept your <u>burnt</u> sacrifice;

4 Grant you your heart's de-<u>sire</u> ♦
and fulfil <u>all</u> your mind.

5 May we rejoice in your salvation:
and triumph in the name of our <u>God</u>; ♦
may the Lord perform <u>all your</u> petitions.

6 Now I know that the Lord will save his a-<u>nointed</u>; ♦
he will answer him from his holy heaven:
with the mighty strength of <u>his</u> right hand.

7 Some put their trust in chariots and some in <u>horses</u>, ♦
but we will call only on the name of the <u>Lord</u> our God.

Glory be to the Father and to the <u>Son</u>; ♦
and to the <u>Holy</u> Spirit;
as it was in the beginning is <u>now</u> ♦
and shall be for <u>ever</u>. Amen.

Psalm 22

David Wilson

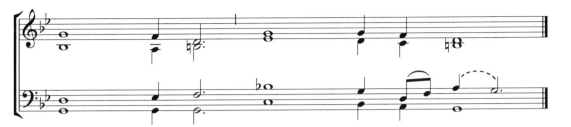

1 My God, my God, why have you for<u>sak</u>en me, ♦
   and are so far from my salvation:
     from the words of <u>my</u> distress?

2 O my God, I cry in the daytime:
     but you do <u>not</u> answer; ♦
   and by night also, but I <u>find</u> no rest.

3 Yet you are the <u>Holy</u> One, ♦
   enthroned upon the <u>praises</u> of Israel.

6 But as for me, I am a worm and <u>no</u> man, ♦
   scorned by all and despised <u>by</u> the people.

7 All who see me laugh me <u>to</u> scorn; ♦
   they curl their lips and wag their <u>heads</u>, saying,

8 'He trusted in the Lord; let him de-<u>liver</u> him; ♦
   let him deliver him, if he de-<u>lights</u> in him.'

17 I can count all <u>my</u> bones; ♦
   they stand staring and <u>looking</u> upon me.

18 They divide my garments a-<u>mong</u> them; ♦
   they cast lots <u>for</u> my clothing.

19 Be not far from me, <u>O</u> Lord; ♦
   you are my strength; <u>hasten</u> to help me.

   Glory be to the Father and to the <u>Son</u>; ♦
   and to the <u>Holy</u> Spirit;
   as it was in the beginning is <u>now</u> ♦
   and shall be for <u>ever</u>. Amen.

Psalm 23

Norman Warren

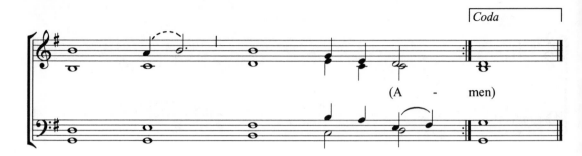

(A - men)

1 The Lord is my <u>she</u>pherd; ♦
therefore can I <u>lack</u> nothing.

2 He makes me lie down in green <u>pa</u>stures ♦
and leads me be<u>side</u> still waters.

3 He shall refresh my <u>soul</u> ♦
and guide me in the paths of righteousness for <u>his</u> name's sake.

4 Though I walk through the valley of the shadow of death,
  I will fear no <u>e</u>-vil; ♦
for you are with me;
  your rod and your staff, they <u>com</u>fort me.

5 You spread a table before me
  in the presence of those who <u>trouble</u> me; ♦
you have anointed my head with oil
  and my cup <u>shall</u> be full.

6 Surely goodness and loving mercy shall follow me
  all the days of my <u>life</u>, ♦
and I will dwell in the house of the <u>Lord</u> for ever. ♦

Glory be to the Father and to the <u>Son</u>; ♦
and to the <u>Ho</u>ly Spirit;
as it was in the beginning is <u>now</u> ♦
and shall be for <u>ever</u>. Amen.

Psalm 24

Barry Ferguson

* Tenors sing B♮ instead of D last time only

1 The earth is the Lord's and all that <u>fills</u> it, ♦
   the compass of the world and all who <u>dwell</u> therein.

2 For he has founded it upon <u>the</u> seas ♦
   and set it firm upon the rivers <u>of</u> the deep.

3 'Who shall ascend the hill of <u>the</u> Lord, ♦
   or who can rise up in his <u>ho</u>-ly place?'

4 'Those who have clean hands and a <u>pure</u> heart, ♦
   who have not lifted up their soul to an idol,
    nor sworn an oath <u>to</u> a lie;

5 'They shall receive a blessing <u>from the</u> Lord, ♦
   a just reward from the God of <u>their</u> salvation.'

6 Such is the company of those <u>who</u> seek him, ♦
   of those who seek your face, O <u>God</u> of Jacob.

7 Lift up your heads, O gates;
    be lifted up, you everlast-<u>ing</u> doors; ♦
   and the King of glory <u>shall</u> come in.

8 'Who is the King <u>of</u> glory?' ♦
   'The Lord, strong and mighty,
    the Lord who is <u>mighty</u> in battle.'

9 Lift up your heads, O gates;
    be lifted up, you everlast-<u>ing</u> doors; ♦
   and the King of glory <u>shall</u> come in.

10 'Who is this King <u>of</u> glory?' ♦
   'The Lord of hosts, he is the <u>King</u> of glory.'

   Glory be to the Father and to the <u>Son</u>; ♦
   and to the <u>Holy</u> Spirit;
   as it was in the beginning is <u>now</u> ♦
   and shall be for <u>ever</u>. Amen.

Psalm 25

Alan Warren

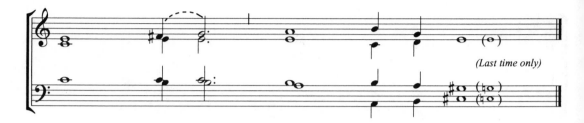

(Last time only)

1 To you, O Lord, I lift up my soul;
 O my God, in you I <u>trust</u>; ♦
 let me not be put to shame;
  let not my enemies triumph <u>o</u>-ver me.

2 Let none who look to you be put to <u>shame</u>, ♦
 but let the treacherous be shamed <u>and</u> frustrated.

3 Make me to know your ways, O <u>Lord</u>, ♦
 and <u>teach me</u> your paths.

4 Lead me in your truth and <u>teach</u> me, ♦
 for you are the God of my salvation;
  for you have I hoped <u>all the</u> day long.

5 Remember, Lord, your compassion and <u>love</u>, ♦
 for they are from <u>e</u>-verlasting.

6 Remember not the sins of my youth
 or my trans<u>gres</u>sions, ♦
 but think on me in your goodness, O Lord,
  according to your <u>stead</u>fast love.

7 Gracious and upright is the <u>Lord</u>; ♦
 therefore shall he teach sinners <u>in</u> the way.

8 He will guide the humble in doing <u>right</u> ♦
 and teach his way <u>to</u> the lowly.

 Glory be to the Father and to the <u>Son</u>; ♦
 and to the <u>Holy</u> Spirit;
 as it was in the beginning is <u>now</u> ♦
 and shall be for <u>ever</u>. Amen.

Psalm 26

Peter White

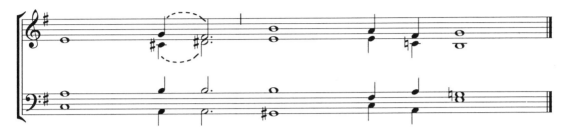

1 Give judgement for me, O Lord,
　　for I have walked with in<u>teg</u>rity; ♦
　I have trusted in the Lord and <u>have</u> not faltered.

2 Test me, O Lord, and <u>try</u> me; ♦
　examine my <u>heart and</u> my mind.

3 For your love is before my <u>eyes</u>; ♦
　I have <u>walked in</u> your truth.

4 I have not joined the company of the <u>false</u>, ♦
　nor consorted <u>with the</u> deceitful.

8 Lord, I love the house of your hab<u>it</u>ation ♦
　and the place where your <u>glory</u> abides.

9 Sweep me not away with <u>sinners</u>, ♦
　nor my life <u>with</u> the bloodthirsty,

10 Whose hands are full of wicked <u>schemes</u> ♦
　and their right hand <u>full</u> of bribes.

11 As for me, I will walk with in<u>teg</u>rity; ♦
　redeem me, Lord, and be <u>merciful</u> to me.

12 My foot stands <u>firm</u>; ♦
　in the great congregation I will <u>bless</u> the Lord.

Glory be to the Father and to the <u>Son</u>; ♦
and to the <u>Ho</u>ly Spirit;
as it was in the beginning is <u>now</u> ♦
and shall be for <u>ever</u>. Amen.

Psalm 27

Norman Warren

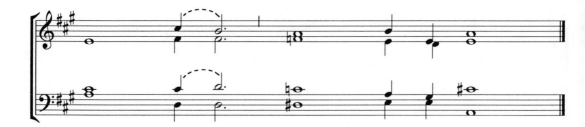

1 The Lord is my light and my salvation;
    whom then shall I <u>fear</u>? ♦
The Lord is the strength of my life;
    of whom then shall I <u>be</u> afraid?

2 When the wicked, even my enemies and my foes,
    came upon me to eat up my <u>flesh</u>, ♦
they <u>stumbled</u> and fell.

3 Though a host encamp against me,
    my heart shall not be a-<u>fraid</u>, ♦
and though there rise up war against me,
    yet will I put my <u>trust</u> in him.

4 One thing have I asked of the Lord
    and that alone I <u>seek</u>: ♦
that I may dwell in the house of the Lord
    all the <u>days of</u> my life,

5 To behold the fair beauty of the <u>Lord</u> ♦
and to seek his will <u>in</u> his temple.

6 For in the day of trouble
    he shall hide me in his <u>shel</u>ter; ♦
in the secret place of his dwelling shall he hide me
    and set me <u>high upon</u> a rock.

7 And now shall he lift up my <u>head</u> ♦
above my enemies <u>round</u> about me;

8 Therefore will I offer in his dwelling an oblation
    with great <u>glad</u>ness; ♦
I will sing and make <u>music</u> to the Lord.

Glory be to the Father and to the <u>Son</u>; ♦
and to the <u>Ho</u>ly Spirit;
as it was in the beginning is <u>now</u> ♦
and shall be for <u>ever</u>. Amen.

Psalm 29

Norman Warren

1 Ascribe to the Lord, you powers of <u>heaven</u>, ◆
   ascribe to the Lord <u>glory</u> and strength.

2 Ascribe to the Lord the honour due to his <u>name</u>; ◆
   worship the Lord in the <u>beauty</u> of holiness.

3 The voice of the Lord is upon the waters;
      the God of glory <u>thunders</u>; ◆
   the Lord is upon the <u>migh</u>-ty waters.

4 The voice of the Lord is mighty in oper<u>ation</u>; ◆
   the voice of the Lord is a <u>glo</u>rious voice.

8 The voice of the Lord makes the oak trees writhe
      and strips the forests <u>bare</u>; ◆
   in his temple <u>all</u> cry, 'Glory!'

9 The Lord sits enthroned above the <u>water flood</u>; ◆
   the Lord sits enthroned as king for <u>ever</u>more.

10 The Lord shall give strength to his <u>people</u>; ◆
   the Lord shall give his people the <u>blessing</u> of peace.

   Glory be to the Father and to the <u>Son</u>; ◆
   and to the <u>Ho</u>ly Spirit;
   as it was in the beginning is <u>now</u> ◆
   and shall be for <u>ever</u>. Amen.

Psalm 30

David Wilson

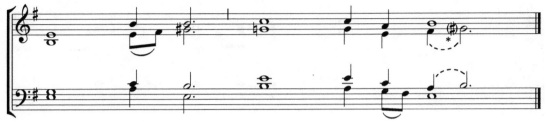

* Altos take G♯ last time only

1   I will exalt you, O Lord,
      because you have raised <u>me</u> up ♦
    and have not let my foes <u>tri</u>umph over me.

2   O Lord my God, I cried out <u>to</u> you ♦
    and <u>you</u> have healed me.

3   You brought me up, O Lord, from <u>the</u> dead; ♦
    you restored me to life from among those
      that go <u>down</u> to the Pit.

4   Sing to the Lord, you servants <u>of</u> his; ♦
    give thanks to his <u>ho</u>-ly name.

5   For his wrath endures but the twinkling of an eye,
      his favour for a <u>life</u>time. ♦
    Heaviness may endure for a night:
      but joy comes <u>in</u> the morning.

11 You have turned my mourning into <u>danc</u>ing; ♦
    you have put off my sackcloth and girded <u>me</u> with gladness;

12 Therefore my heart sings to you without <u>ceas</u>ing; ♦
    O Lord my God, I will give you <u>thanks</u> for ever.

    Glory be to the Father and to the <u>Son</u>; ♦
    and to the <u>Ho</u>ly Spirit;
    as it was in the beginning is <u>now</u> ♦
    and shall be for <u>ever</u>. Amen.

Psalm 31

Alan Warren

1 In you, O Lord, have I taken refuge;
   let me never be put <u>to</u> shame; ◆
deliver me <u>in</u> your righteousness.

2 Incline your ear <u>to</u> me; ◆
make haste <u>to</u> deliver me.

3 Be my strong rock, a fortress to save me,
   for you are my rock and <u>my</u> stronghold; ◆
guide me, and lead me <u>for</u> your name's sake.

4 Take me out of the net
   that they have laid secretly <u>for</u> me, ◆
for <u>you are</u> my strength.

5 Into your hands I commend <u>my</u> spirit, ◆
for you have redeemed me, O Lord <u>God</u> of truth.

6 I hate those who cling to <u>worthless</u> idols; ◆
I put my trust <u>in</u> the Lord.

7 I will be glad and rejoice in <u>your</u> mercy, ◆
for you have seen my affliction
   and known my soul <u>in</u> adversity.

8 You have not shut me up in the hand of <u>the</u> enemy; ◆
you have set my feet in an <u>o</u>-pen place.

23 Love the Lord, all you <u>his</u> servants; ◆
   for the Lord protects the faithful;
      but repays to the <u>full</u> the proud.

24 Be strong and let your heart <u>take</u> courage, ◆
all you who wait in hope <u>for</u> the Lord.

   Glory be to the Father and to the <u>Son</u>; ◆
   and to the <u>Holy</u> Spirit;
   as it was in the beginning is <u>now</u> ◆
   and shall be for <u>ever</u>. Amen.

Psalm 32

Norman Warren

1 Happy the one whose transgression is for<u>gi</u>ven, ♦
and whose <u>sin</u> is covered.

2 Happy the one to whom the Lord imputes no <u>guilt</u>, ♦
and in whose spirit <u>there is</u> no guile.

3 For I held my <u>tongue</u>; ♦
my bones wasted away
    through my groaning <u>all the</u> day long.

4 Your hand was heavy upon me day and <u>night</u>; ♦
my moisture was dried up like the <u>drought</u> in summer.

5 Then I acknowledged my sin to <u>you</u> ♦
and my iniquity I <u>did</u> not hide.

6 I said, 'I will confess my transgressions to the <u>Lord</u>,' ♦
and you forgave the <u>guilt of</u> my sin.

7 Therefore let all the faithful make their prayers to you
    in time of <u>trouble</u>; ♦
in the great water flood, it <u>shall</u> not reach them.

8 You are a place for me to <u>hide</u> in; ♦
you preserve me from trouble;
    you surround me with <u>songs of</u> deliverance.

Glory be to the Father and to the <u>Son</u>; ♦
and to the <u>Holy</u> Spirit;
as it was in the beginning is <u>now</u> ♦
and shall be for <u>ever</u>. Amen.

Psalm 33

Barry Ferguson

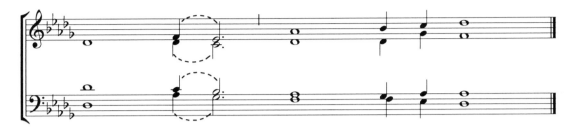

1 Rejoice in the Lord, O you <u>right</u>-eous, ♦
   for it is good for the <u>just to</u> sing praises.

2 Praise the Lord with the <u>lyre</u>; ♦
   on the ten-stringed harp <u>sing</u> his praise.

3 Sing for him a <u>new</u> song; ♦
   play skilfully, with <u>shouts</u> of praise.

4 For the word of the Lord is <u>true</u> ♦
   and all his <u>works</u> are sure.

5 He loves righteousness and <u>jus</u>tice; ♦
   the earth is full of the loving-kindness <u>of</u> the Lord.

6 By the word of the Lord were the heavens <u>made</u> ♦
   and all their host by the <u>breath of</u> his mouth.

7 He gathers up the waters of the sea as in a <u>water</u>skin ♦
   and lays up the deep <u>in</u> his treasury.

8 Let all the earth fear the <u>Lord</u>; ♦
   stand in awe of him, all who <u>dwell in</u> the world.

   Glory be to the Father and to the <u>Son</u>; ♦
   and to the <u>Ho</u>ly Spirit;
   as it was in the beginning is <u>now</u> ♦
   and shall be for <u>ever</u>. Amen.

Psalm 34

Peter White

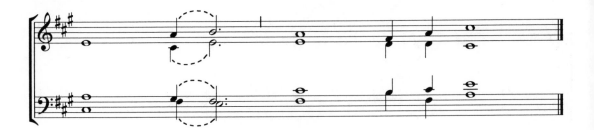

1 I will bless the Lord at <u>all</u> times; ♦
   his praise shall ever be <u>in</u> my mouth.

2 My soul shall glory in the <u>Lord</u>; ♦
   let the humble <u>hear and</u> be glad.

3 O magnify the Lord <u>with</u> me; ♦
   let us exalt his <u>name</u> together.

4 I sought the Lord and he <u>answered</u> me ♦
   and delivered me from <u>all</u> my fears.

5 Look upon him and be <u>ra</u>-diant ♦
   and your faces shall <u>not be</u> ashamed.

6 This poor soul cried, and the Lord <u>heard</u> me ♦
   and saved me from <u>all</u> my troubles.

7 The angel of the Lord encamps around those who <u>fear</u> him ♦
   and de-<u>liv</u>ers them.

8 O taste and see that the Lord is <u>gra</u>cious; ♦
   blessed is the one who <u>trusts</u> in him.

   Glory be to the Father and to the <u>Son</u>; ♦
   and to the <u>Holy</u> Spirit;
   as it was in the beginning is <u>now</u> ♦
   and shall be for <u>ever</u>. Amen.

Psalm 36

Norman Warren

1 Sin whispers to the wicked, in the depths of their heart; ♦
  there is no fear of God be-fore their eyes.

2 They flatter themselves in their own eyes ♦
  that their abominable sin will not be found out.

3 The words of their mouth are unrighteous and full of deceit; ♦
  they have ceased to act wisely and to do good.

4 They think out mischief upon their beds
    and have set themselves in no good way; ♦
  nor do they abhor that which is evil.

5 Your love, O Lord, reaches to the heavens ♦
  and your faithfulness to the clouds.

6 Your righteousness stands like the strong mountains,
    your justice like the great deep; ♦
  you, Lord, shall save both man and beast.

7 How precious is your loving mercy, O God! ♦
  All mortal flesh shall take refuge
    under the shadow of your wings.

8 They shall be satisfied with the abundance of your house; ♦
  they shall drink from the river of your delights.

9 For with you is the well of life ♦
  and in your light shall we see light.

  Glory be to the Father and to the Son; ♦
  and to the Holy Spirit;
  as it was in the beginning is now ♦
  and shall be for ever. Amen.

Psalm 37

John Barnard

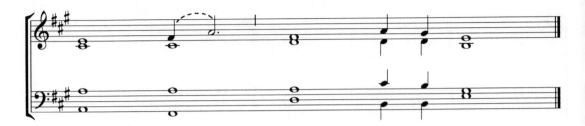

1 Fret not because of evil<u>do</u>ers; ♦
   be not jealous of <u>those who</u> do wrong.

2 For they shall soon wither like <u>grass</u> ♦
   and like the green herb <u>fade</u> away.

3 Trust in the Lord and be doing <u>good</u>; ♦
   dwell in the land and be <u>nourished</u> with truth.

4 Let your delight be in the <u>Lord</u> ♦
   and he will give you your <u>heart's</u> desire.

5 Commit your way to the Lord and put your trust in <u>him</u>, ♦
   and he will <u>bring it</u> to pass.

6 He will make your righteousness as clear as the <u>light</u> ♦
   and your just dealing <u>as</u> the noonday.

7 Be still before the Lord and wait for <u>him</u>; ♦
   do not fret over those that prosper
      as they follow their <u>e</u>-vil schemes.

8 Refrain from anger and abandon <u>wrath</u>; ♦
   do not fret, lest you be <u>moved to</u> do evil.

9 For evildoers shall be cut <u>off</u>, ♦
   but those who wait upon the Lord shall pos<u>sess</u> the land.

   Glory be to the Father and to the <u>Son</u>; ♦
   and to the <u>Holy</u> Spirit;
   as it was in the beginning is <u>now</u> ♦
   and shall be for <u>ever</u>. Amen.

Psalm 40

Barry Ferguson

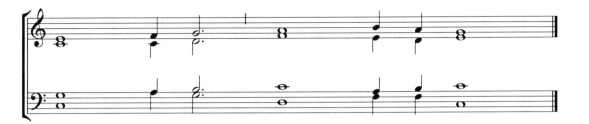

1 I waited patiently <u>for the</u> Lord; ♦
   he inclined to me and <u>heard</u> my cry.

2 He brought me out of the roaring pit:
     out of the mire <u>and</u> clay; ♦
   he set my feet upon a rock and made my <u>foot</u>-ing sure.

3 He has put a new song in my mouth,
     a song of praise to <u>our</u> God; ♦
   many shall see and fear
     and put their <u>trust in</u> the Lord.

4 Blessed is the one who trusts in <u>the</u> Lord, ♦
   who does not turn to the proud that <u>follow</u> a lie.

5 Great are the wonders you have done, O Lord my God:
     how great your designs <u>for</u> us! ♦
   There is none that can be com-<u>pared</u> with you.

6 If I were to proclaim them and <u>tell of</u> them ♦
   they would be more than I am able <u>to</u> express.

   Glory be to the Father and to the <u>Son</u>; ♦
   and to the <u>Holy</u> Spirit;
   as it was in the beginning is <u>now</u> ♦
   and shall be for <u>ever</u>. Amen.

Psalm 41

Peter White

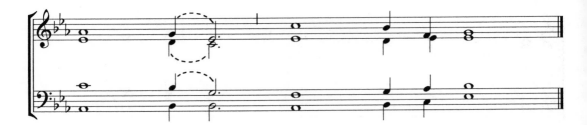

1 Blessed are those who consider the poor and <u>nee</u>dy; ◆
 the Lord will deliver them in the <u>time</u> of trouble.

2 The Lord preserves them and restores their life,
 that they may be happy <u>in</u> the land; ◆
 he will not hand them over to the <u>will of</u> their enemies.

3 The Lord sustains them on their <u>sick</u>bed; ◆
 their sickness, Lord, <u>you will</u> remove.

4 And so I said, 'Lord, be merciful <u>to</u> me; ◆
 heal me, for I have <u>sinned a</u>-gainst you.'

10 But you, O Lord, be merciful <u>to</u> me ◆
 and raise me up, that <u>I may</u> reward them.

11 By this I know that you <u>favour</u> me, ◆
 that my enemy does not <u>tri</u>umph over me.

12 Because of my integrity you up<u>hold</u> me ◆
 and will set me before your <u>face</u> for ever.

13 Blessed be the Lord God <u>of</u> Israel, ◆
 from everlasting to everlasting. <u>Amen</u> and Amen.

 Glory be to the Father and to the <u>Son</u>; ◆
 and to the <u>Ho</u>ly Spirit;
 as it was in the beginning is <u>now</u> ◆
 and shall be for <u>ever</u>. Amen.

Psalm 42

Norman Warren

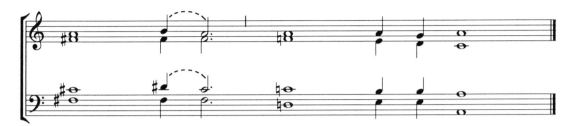

1 As the deer longs for the <u>wat</u>er brooks, ♦
   so longs my soul for <u>you</u>, O God.

2 My soul is athirst for God, even for the living <u>God</u>; ♦
   when shall I come to behold the <u>face</u> of God?

3 My tears have been my bread day and <u>night</u>, ♦
   while all day long they say to me, 'Where is <u>now</u> your God?'

4 Now when I think on these things, I pour out my <u>soul</u>: ♦
   how I went with the multitude:
     and led the procession to the <u>house</u> of God,

5 With the voice of praise and <u>thanks</u>giving, ♦
   among those who kept <u>ho</u>-ly day.

6 *Why are you so full of heaviness, O my <u>soul</u>, ♦*
   and why are you so dis<u>quieted</u> within me?

7 *O put your trust in <u>God</u>; ♦*
   for I will yet give him thanks;
     who is the help of my countenance, <u>and</u> my God.

   Glory be to the Father and to the <u>Son</u>; ♦
   and to the <u>Ho</u>ly Spirit;
   as it was in the beginning is <u>now</u> ♦
   and shall be for <u>ev</u>er. Amen.

Psalm 43

Norman Warren

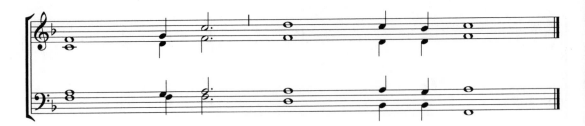

1   Give judgement for me, O God:
     and defend my cause against an un<u>god</u>ly people; ♦
  deliver me from the deceitful <u>and</u> the wicked.

2   For you are the God of my refuge;
     why have you cast <u>me</u> from you, ♦
  and why go I so heavily, while the <u>enemy</u> oppresses me?

3   O send out your light and your truth, that <u>they may</u> lead me, ♦
  and bring me to your holy hill and <u>to</u> your dwelling,

4   That I may go to the altar of God,
     to the God of my <u>joy and</u> gladness; ♦
  and on the lyre I will give thanks to you, O <u>God</u> my God.

5   *Why are you so full of heaviness, <u>O my</u> soul,* ♦
  and why are you so dis<u>quieted</u> within me?

6   *O put your trust in <u>God</u>;* ♦
  for I will yet give him thanks;
     who is the help of my countenance, <u>and</u> my God.

  Glory be to the Father and to the <u>Son</u>; ♦
  and to the <u>Holy</u> Spirit;
  as it was in the beginning is <u>now</u> ♦
  and shall be for <u>ever</u>. Amen.

Psalm 45

Noël Tredinnick

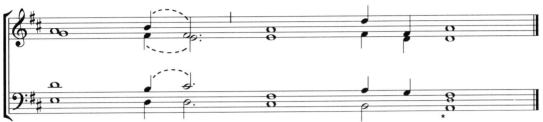

* Basses sing D not A on final chord

1 My heart is astir with gracious <u>words</u>; ♦
   as I make my song for the king,
     my tongue is the pen of a <u>rea</u>dy writer.

2 You are the fairest of <u>men</u>; ♦
   full of grace are your lips,
     for God has <u>blest you</u> for ever.

3 Gird your sword upon your thigh, O <u>mighty</u> one; ♦
   gird on your <u>majesty</u> and glory.

4 Ride on and prosper in the cause of <u>truth</u> ♦
   and for the sake of hu-<u>mility</u> and righteousness.

5 Your right hand will teach you terrible <u>things</u>; ♦
   your arrows will be sharp in the heart of the king's enemies,
     so that peoples <u>fall</u> beneath you.

6 Your throne is God's throne, for <u>ever</u>; ♦
   the sceptre of your kingdom is the <u>sceptre</u> of righteousness.

7 You love righteousness and hate in-<u>iqui</u>-ty; ♦
   therefore God, your God, has anointed you
     with the oil of gladness <u>a</u>-bove your fellows.

   Glory be to the Father and to the <u>Son</u>; ♦
   and to the <u>Holy</u> Spirit;
   as it was in the beginning is <u>now</u> ♦
   and shall be for <u>ever</u>. Amen.

Psalm 46

Norman Warren

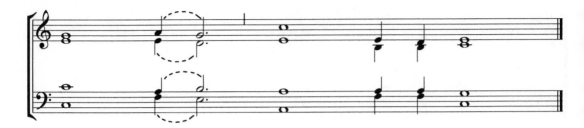

1 God is our refuge and <u>strength</u>, ♦
   a very present <u>help</u> in trouble;

2 Therefore we will not fear, though the earth be <u>moved</u>, ♦
   and though the mountains tremble in the <u>heart</u> of the sea;

3 Though the waters rage and <u>swell</u>, ♦
   and though the mountains quake at the <u>towe</u>ring seas.

4 There is a river whose streams make glad the city of <u>God</u>, ♦
   the holy place of the dwelling <u>of the</u> Most High.

5 God is in the midst of her;
     therefore shall she not be re<u>moved</u>; ♦
   God shall help her at the <u>break</u> of day.

6 The nations are in uproar and the kingdoms are <u>sha</u>-ken, ♦
   but God utters his voice and the earth shall <u>melt</u> away.

10 'Be still, and know that <u>I am</u> God; ♦
   I will be exalted among the nations;
     I will be exalted <u>in</u> the earth.'

11 The Lord of hosts is <u>with</u> us; ♦
   the God of Jacob <u>is</u> our stronghold.

   Glory be to the Father and to the <u>Son</u>; ♦
   and to the <u>Holy</u> Spirit;
   as it was in the beginning is <u>now</u> ♦
   and shall be for <u>ever</u>. Amen.

Psalm 47

Barry Ferguson

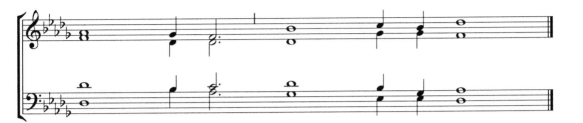

1 Clap your hands together, <u>all you</u> peoples; ♦
   O sing to God with <u>shouts</u> of joy.

2 For the Lord Most High is to <u>be</u> feared; ♦
   he is the great King over <u>all</u> the earth.

3 He subdued the peoples <u>under</u> us ♦
   and the nations <u>under</u> our feet.

4 He has chosen our heritage <u>for</u> us, ♦
   the pride of Jacob, <u>whom</u> he loves.

5 God has gone up with a <u>merry</u> noise, ♦
   the Lord with the <u>sound of</u> the trumpet.

6 O sing praises to God, <u>sing</u> praises; ♦
   sing praises to our <u>King</u>, sing praises.

7 For God is the King of all <u>the</u> earth; ♦
   sing praises with <u>all</u> your skill.

8 God reigns over the <u>na</u>-tions; ♦
   God has taken his seat upon his <u>ho</u>-ly throne.

   Glory be to the Father and to the <u>Son</u>; ♦
   and to the <u>Ho</u>ly Spirit;
   as it was in the beginning is <u>now</u> ♦
   and shall be for <u>ever</u>. Amen.

Psalm 48

John Barnard

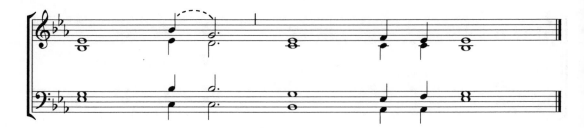

1 Great is the Lord and highly to be <u>praised</u>, ♦
   in the city <u>of</u> our God.

2 His holy mountain is fair and lifted <u>high</u>, ♦
   the joy of <u>all</u> the earth.

3 On Mount Zion, the divine <u>dwelling</u> place, ♦
   stands the city of the <u>great</u> king.

4 In her palaces God has <u>shown him</u>self ♦
   to be a <u>sure</u> refuge.

9 We have waited on your loving-kindness, O <u>God</u>, ♦
   in the <u>midst of</u> your temple.

10 As with your name, O God;
    so your praise reaches to the ends of the <u>earth</u>; ♦
    your right hand is <u>full</u> of justice.

11 Let Mount Zion rejoice and the daughters of Judah be <u>glad</u>, ♦
    because of your <u>judgements</u>, O Lord.

12 Walk about Zion and go round about her;
    count all her <u>towers</u>; ♦
    consider well her bulwarks; pass <u>through</u> her citadels,

13 That you may tell those who come after;
    that such is our God for ever and <u>e</u>-ver. ♦
    It is he that shall be our guide for <u>ever</u>more.

    Glory be to the Father and to the <u>Son</u>; ♦
    and to the <u>Ho</u>ly Spirit;
    as it was in the beginning is <u>now</u> ♦
    and shall be for <u>ever</u>. Amen.

Psalm 50

Peter White

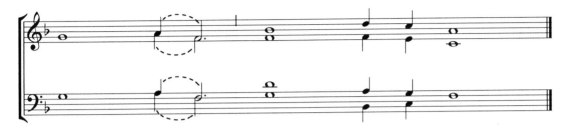

1 The Lord, the most mighty God, has <u>spo</u>ken ♦
    and called the world from the rising of the sun <u>to</u> its setting.

2 Out of Zion, perfect in beauty, God shines <u>forth</u>; ♦
    our God comes and will <u>not</u> keep silence.

3 Consuming fire goes out be<u>fore</u> him ♦
    and a mighty tempest <u>stirs</u> about him.

4 He calls the heaven a-<u>bove</u>, ♦
    and the earth, that he may <u>judge</u> his people:

5 'Gather to me my <u>faith</u>ful, ♦
    who have sealed my <u>covenant</u> with sacrifice.'

6 Let the heavens declare his <u>right</u>eousness, ♦
    for God him<u>self</u> is judge.

14 'Offer to God a sacrifice of <u>thanks</u>giving ♦
    and fulfil your vows to <u>God</u> Most High.

15 'Call upon me in the day of <u>trou</u>ble; ♦
    I will deliver you and <u>you</u> shall honour me.'

    Glory be to the Father and to the <u>Son</u>; ♦
    and to the <u>Ho</u>ly Spirit;
    as it was in the beginning is <u>now</u> ♦
    and shall be for <u>ever</u>. Amen.

Psalm 51

Norman Warren

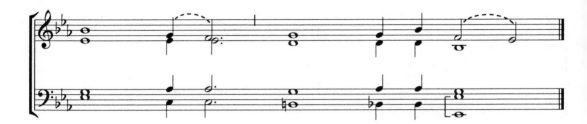

1 Have mercy on me, O God, in your great <u>good</u>ness; ♦
   according to the abundance of your compassion:
     blot out <u>my</u> offences.

2 Wash me thoroughly from my <u>wicked</u>ness ♦
   and cleanse me <u>from</u> my sin.

3 For I acknowledge my <u>faults</u> ♦
   and my sin is <u>ever</u> before me.

4 Against you only have I <u>sinned</u> ♦
   and done what is evil <u>in</u> your sight,

10 Turn your face from my <u>sins</u> ♦
    and blot out <u>all my</u> misdeeds.

11 Make me a clean heart, O <u>God</u>, ♦
    and renew a right <u>spir</u>it within me.

12 Cast me not away from your <u>pres</u>ence ♦
    and take not your holy <u>spirit</u> from me.

13 Give me again the joy of your sal<u>va</u>tion ♦
    and sustain me with your <u>gra</u>cious spirit;

   Glory be to the Father and to the <u>Son</u>; ♦
   and to the <u>Ho</u>ly Spirit;
   as it was in the beginning is <u>now</u> ♦
   and shall be for <u>ever</u>. Amen.

Psalm 52

David Wilson

1 Why do you glory in evil, <u>you</u> tyrant, ♦
  while the goodness of God en<u>dures</u> continually?

2 You plot destruction, you de<u>cei</u>ver; ♦
  your tongue is like a <u>sharp</u>ened razor.

3 You love evil rather <u>than</u> good, ♦
  falsehood rather than the <u>word</u> of truth.

4 You love all words <u>that</u> hurt, ♦
  O you de<u>ceit</u>ful tongue.

5 Therefore God shall utterly bring <u>you</u> down; ♦
  he shall take you and pluck you out of your tent
    and root you out of the <u>land of</u> the living.

6 The righteous shall see this <u>and</u> tremble; ♦
  they shall laugh you to <u>scorn</u>, and say:

7 'This is the one who did not take God <u>for a</u> refuge, ♦
  but trusted in great riches and <u>relied up</u>-on wickedness.'

8 But I am like a spreading olive tree in the house <u>of</u> God; ♦
  I trust in the goodness of God for <u>ever</u> and ever.

9 I will always give thanks to you for what you <u>have</u> done; ♦
  I will hope in your name,
    for your faithful ones de<u>light</u> in it.

  Glory be to the Father and to the <u>Son</u>; ♦
  and to the <u>Holy</u> Spirit;
  as it was in the beginning is <u>now</u> ♦
  and shall be for <u>ever</u>. Amen.

Psalm 62

Norman Warren

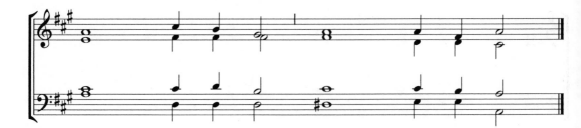

1 On God alone my soul in <u>still</u>ness waits; ♦
   from him comes <u>my</u> salvation.

2 He alone is my rock and <u>my</u> salvation, ♦
   my stronghold, so that I shall <u>never</u> be shaken.

3 How long will all of you assail me <u>to</u> destroy me, ♦
   as you would a tottering wall or a <u>lean</u>ing fence?

4 They plot only to thrust me down from my place of honour;
      lies are their <u>chief</u> delight; ♦
   they bless with their mouth, but in their <u>heart</u> they curse.

5 Wait on God alone in stillness, <u>O</u> my soul; ♦
   for in him <u>is</u> my hope.

6 He alone is my rock and <u>my</u> salvation, ♦
   my stronghold, so that I shall <u>not</u> be shaken.

7 In God is my strength <u>and</u> my glory; ♦
   God is my strong rock; in him <u>is</u> my refuge.

8 Put your trust in him <u>always</u>, my people; ♦
   pour out your hearts before him, for <u>God</u> is our refuge.

   Glory be to the Father and to the <u>Son</u>; ♦
   and to the <u>Ho</u>ly Spirit;
   as it was in the beginning is <u>now</u> ♦
   and shall be for <u>ever</u>. Amen.

Psalm 63

Norman Warren

1   O God, you are my God; eagerly I <u>seek</u> you; ◆
     my soul is a-<u>thirst</u> for you.

2   My flesh also faints <u>for</u> you, ◆
     as in a dry and thirsty land where there <u>is</u> no water.

3   So would I gaze upon you in your holy <u>place</u>, ◆
     that I might behold your <u>power and</u> your glory.

4   Your loving-kindness is better than life it<u>self</u> ◆
     and so my <u>lips</u> shall praise you.

5   I will bless you as long as I <u>live</u> ◆
     and lift up my <u>hands in</u> your name.

6   My soul shall be satisfied, as with marrow and <u>fatness</u>, ◆
     and my mouth shall praise you with <u>joy</u>ful lips,

     Glory be to the Father and to the <u>Son</u>; ◆
     and to the <u>Ho</u>ly Spirit;
     as it was in the beginning is <u>now</u> ◆
     and shall be for <u>ever</u>. Amen.

Psalm 65

John Barnard

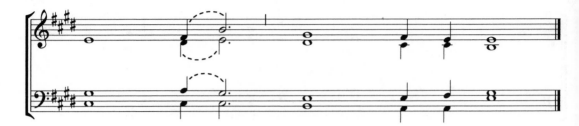

1 Praise is due to you, O God, in Zi-on; ♦
   to you that answer prayer shall vows be paid.

8 You visit the earth and water it; ♦
   you make it very plenteous.

9 The river of God is full of water; ♦
   you prepare grain for your people:
   for so you provide for the earth.

10 You drench the furrows and smooth out the ridges; ♦
   you soften the ground with showers and bless its increase.

11 You crown the year with your goodness, ♦
   and your paths overflow with plenty.

12 May the pastures of the wilderness flow with goodness ♦
   and the hills be girded with joy.

13 May the meadows be clothed with flocks of sheep ♦
   and the valleys stand so thick with corn:
   that they shall laugh and sing.

   Glory be to the Father and to the Son; ♦
   and to the Holy Spirit;
   as it was in the beginning is now ♦
   and shall be for ever. Amen.

Psalm 66

Barry Ferguson

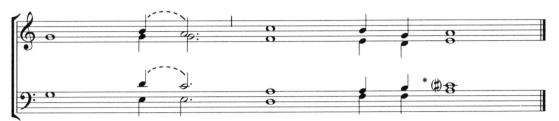

Tenors take C♯ last time only

1 Be joyful in God, all the <u>earth</u>; ♦
  sing the glory of his name;
    sing the glory <u>of</u> his praise.

2 Say to God, 'How awesome are <u>your</u> deeds! ♦
  Because of your great strength:
    your enemies shall <u>bow</u> before you.

3 'All the earth shall <u>worship</u> you, ♦
  sing to you, sing <u>praise to</u> your name.'

4 Come now and behold the works of <u>God</u>, ♦
  how wonderful he is in his dealings with <u>hu</u>-mankind.

5 He turned the sea into dry land;
    the river they passed through on <u>foot</u>; ♦
  there we re-<u>joiced</u> in him.

6 In his might he rules for ever:
    his eyes keep watch over the <u>nations</u>; ♦
  let no rebel rise <u>up</u> against him.

7 Bless our God, O you <u>peoples</u>; ♦
  make the voice of his <u>praise to</u> be heard,

  Glory be to the Father and to the <u>Son</u>; ♦
  and to the <u>Holy</u> Spirit;
  as it was in the beginning is <u>now</u> ♦
  and shall be for <u>ever</u>. Amen.

Psalm 67

Norman Warren

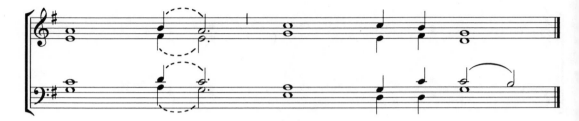

1 God be gracious to us and <u>bless</u> us ♦
  and shew us the light of his countenance,
   and be merciful <u>un</u>to us:

2 That thy way may be known upon <u>earth</u>, ♦
  thy saving health a-<u>mong</u> all nations.

3 Let the people praise you, O <u>God</u>; ♦
  let all the <u>peo</u>-ple praise you.

4 O let the nations rejoice and be <u>glad</u>, ♦
  for thou shalt judge the folk righteously:
   and govern the <u>nations u</u>-pon earth.

5 Let the people praise you, O <u>God</u>; ♦
  yea, let all the <u>peo</u>-ple praise you.

6 Then shall the earth bring forth her <u>increase</u>, ♦
  and God, even our own God, shall <u>give us</u> his blessing.

7 God will <u>bless</u> us, ♦
  and all the ends of the <u>world</u> shall fear him.

  Glory be to the Father and to the <u>Son</u>; ♦
  and to the <u>Ho</u>ly Spirit;
  as it was in the beginning is <u>now</u> ♦
  and shall be for <u>ever</u>. Amen.

Psalm 68

Peter White

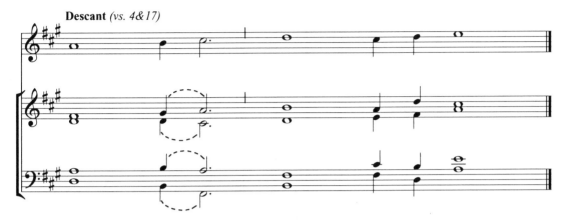

Descant *(vs. 4 & 17)*

1 Let God arise and let his enemies be <u>scat</u>tered; ♦
  let those that hate him <u>flee</u> before him.

2 As the smoke vanishes, so may they vanish <u>a</u>-way; ♦
  as wax melts at the fire:
     so let the wicked perish at the <u>presence</u> of God.

3 But let the righteous be glad and rejoice before <u>God</u>; ♦
  let them make <u>merry</u> with gladness.

4 Sing to God, sing praises to his name;
     exalt him who rides <u>on the</u> clouds. ♦
  The Lord is his name; re-<u>joice be</u>-fore him.

14 You mighty mountain, great mountain <u>of</u> Bashan! ♦
   You towering mountain, great <u>mountain</u> of Bashan!

15 Why look with envy, you towering mountains,
     at the mount which God has desired for his <u>dwell</u>ing, ♦
   the place where the Lord will <u>dwell</u> for ever?

16 The chariots of God are twice ten thousand:
     even thousands upon <u>thou</u>sands; ♦
   the Lord is among them, the Lord of Sinai in <u>ho</u>-ly power.

17 You have gone up on high and led captivity <u>cap</u>tive; ♦
   you have received tribute, even from those who rebelled:
      that you may reign as <u>Lord</u> and God.

   Glory be to the Father and to the <u>Son</u>; ♦
   and to the <u>Holy</u> Spirit;
   as it was in the beginning is <u>now</u> ♦
   and shall be for <u>ever</u>. Amen.

Psalm 70

Norman Warren

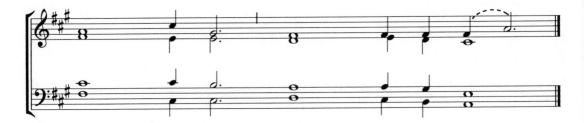

1 O God, make speed to <u>save</u> me; ♦
   O Lord, make <u>haste</u> to help me.

2 Let those who seek my life
      be put to shame and con<u>fus</u>ion; ♦
   let them be turned back and disgraced
      who <u>wish</u> me evil.

3 Let those who mock and de<u>ride</u> me ♦
   turn back be<u>cause of</u> their shame.

4 But let all who seek you rejoice and be <u>glad in</u> you; ♦
   let those who love your salvation say always,
      '<u>Great is</u> the Lord!'

5 As for me, I am poor and <u>needy</u>; ♦
   come to me <u>quickly</u>, O God.

6 You are my help and my de<u>liv</u>erer; ♦
   O Lord, do <u>not</u> delay.

   Glory be to the Father and to the <u>Son</u>; ♦
   and to the <u>Ho</u>ly Spirit;
   as it was in the beginning is <u>now</u> ♦
   and shall be for <u>ever</u>. Amen.

Psalm 71

David Wilson

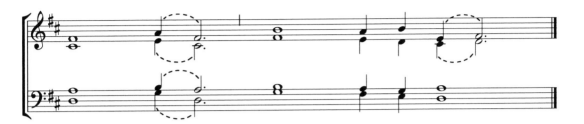

1 In you, O Lord, do I seek <u>re</u>fuge; ♦
   let me never be <u>put</u> to shame.

2 In your righteousness, deliver me and set me <u>free</u>; ♦
   incline your ear to <u>me</u> and save me.

3 Be for me a stronghold to which I may ever re<u>sort</u>; ♦
   send out to save me, for you are my rock <u>and</u> my fortress.

4 Deliver me, my God, from the hand of the <u>wick</u>ed, ♦
   from the grasp of the evildoer <u>and the</u> oppressor.

5 For you are my hope, O Lord <u>God</u>, ♦
   my confidence, even <u>from</u> my youth.

6 Upon you have I leaned from my birth,
      when you drew me from my mother's <u>womb</u>; ♦
   my praise shall be <u>always</u> of you.

7 I have become a portent to <u>many</u>, ♦
   but you are my refuge <u>and</u> my strength.

8 Let my mouth be full of your <u>praise</u> ♦
   and your glory <u>all the</u> day long.

   Glory be to the Father and to the <u>Son</u>; ♦
   and to the <u>Holy</u> Spirit;
   as it was in the beginning is <u>now</u> ♦
   and shall be for <u>ever</u>. Amen.

Psalm 72

David Wilson

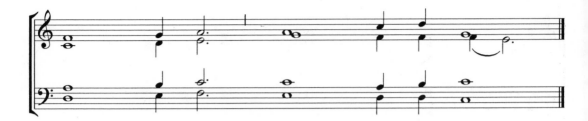

1 Give the king your judgements, O God, ♦
and your righteousness to the son of a king.

2 Then shall he judge your people righteously ♦
and your poor with justice.

3 May the mountains bring forth peace, ♦
and the little hills righteousness for the people.

4 May he defend the poor among the people, ♦
deliver the children of the needy and crush the oppressor.

5 May he live as long as the sun and moon endure, ♦
from one generation to another.

6 May he come down like rain upon the mown grass, ♦
like the showers that water the earth.

7 In his time shall righteousness flourish, ♦
and abundance of peace:
   till the moon shall be no more.

15 Long may he live:
   unto him may be given gold from Sheba; ♦
may prayer be made for him continually:
   and may they bless him all the day long.

Glory be to the Father and to the Son; ♦
and to the Holy Spirit;
as it was in the beginning is now ♦
and shall be for ever. Amen.

Psalm 77

John Barnard

1 I cry aloud to God; ♦
   I cry aloud to God and he will hear me.

2 In the day of my trouble I have sought the Lord; ♦
   by night my hand is stretched out and does not tire;
       my soul refuses comfort.

3 I think upon God and I groan; ♦
   I ponder, and my spirit faints.

4 You will not let my eyelids close; ♦
   I am so troubled that I cannot speak.

5 I consider the days of old; ♦
   I remember the years long past;

6 I commune with my heart in the night; ♦
   my spirit searches for understanding.

11 I will remember the works of the Lord ♦
    and call to mind your wonders of old time.

12 I will meditate on all your works ♦
    and ponder your mighty deeds.

13 Your way, O God, is holy; ♦
    who is so great a god as our God?

    Glory be to the Father and to the Son; ♦
    and to the Holy Spirit;
    as it was in the beginning is now ♦
    and shall be for ever. Amen.

Psalm 78

Norman Warren

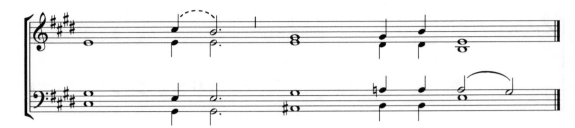

1 Hear my teaching, O my people; ♦
   incline your ears to the words of my mouth.

2 I will open my mouth in a parable; ♦
   I will pour forth mysteries from of old,

3 Such as we have heard and known, ♦
   which our forebears have told us.

4 We will not hide from their children,
      but will recount to generations to come, ♦
   the praises of the Lord and his power:
      and the wonderful works he has done.

5 He laid a solemn charge on Jacob:
      and made it a law in Israel, ♦
   which he commanded them to teach their children,

6 That the generations to come might know:
      and the children yet unborn, ♦
   that they in turn might tell it to their children;

7 So that they might put their trust in God ♦
   and not forget the deeds of God:
      but keep his commandments,

   Glory be to the Father and to the Son; ♦
   and to the Holy Spirit;
   as it was in the beginning is now ♦
   and shall be for ever. Amen.

Psalm 79

Barry Ferguson

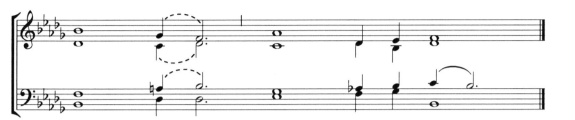

1 O God, the heathen have come into your <u>heri</u>tage; ♦
   your holy temple have they defiled:
      and made Jerusalem a <u>heap</u> of stones.

2 The dead bodies of your servants they have given
      to be food for the birds of the <u>air</u>, ♦
   and the flesh of your faithful to the <u>beasts of</u> the field.

3 Their blood have they shed like water
      on every side of Je<u>ru</u>salem, ♦
   and there was <u>no one</u> to bury them.

4 We have become the taunt of our <u>neigh</u>bours, ♦
   the scorn and derision of those that are <u>round</u> about us.

5 Lord, how long will you be angry, for <u>e</u>-ver? ♦
   How long will your jealous fury <u>blaze</u> like fire?

9 Help us, O God of our salvation, for the glory of your <u>name</u>; ♦
   deliver us, and wipe away our sins for <u>your</u> name's sake.

   Glory be to the Father and to the <u>Son</u>; ♦
   and to the <u>Ho</u>ly Spirit;
   as it was in the beginning is <u>now</u> ♦
   and shall be for <u>ever</u>. Amen.

Psalm 80

Peter White

1 Hear, O Shepherd of Isra-el, ♦
you that led Joseph like a flock;

2 Shine forth, you that are enthroned upon the cherubim, ♦
before Ephraim, Benjamin and Manasseh.

3 Stir up your mighty strength ♦
and come to our salvation.

4 *Turn us again, O God; ♦*
show the light of your countenance, and we shall be saved.

5 O Lord God of hosts, ♦
how long will you be angry at your people's prayer?

6 You feed them with the bread of tears; ♦
you give them abundance of tears to drink.

7 You have made us the derision of our neighbours, ♦
and our enemies laugh us to scorn.

8 *Turn us again, O God of hosts; ♦*
show the light of your countenance, and we shall be saved.

Glory be to the Father and to the Son; ♦
and to the Holy Spirit;
as it was in the beginning is now ♦
and shall be for ever. Amen.

Psalm 81

Norman Warren

1 Sing merrily to God our <u>strength</u>, ♦
shout for joy to the <u>God</u> of Jacob.

2 Take up the song and sound the <u>tim</u>brel, ♦
the tuneful <u>lyre with</u> the harp.

3 Blow the trumpet at the <u>new</u> moon, ♦
as at the full moon, upon our <u>sol</u>emn feast day.

4 For this is a statute for <u>Is</u>ra-el, ♦
a law of the <u>God</u> of Jacob,

6 I heard a voice I did not know, that <u>said</u>: ♦
'I eased their shoulder from the burden;
   their hands were set free from <u>bearing</u> the load.

7 'You called upon me in trouble and I deli<u>vered</u> you; ♦
I answered you from the secret place of thunder:
   and proved you at the <u>waters</u> of Meribah.

8 'Hear, O my people, and I will ad<u>monish</u> you: ♦
O Israel, if you would but <u>listen</u> to me!

9 'There shall be no strange god a-<u>mong</u> you; ♦
you shall not worship a <u>foreign</u> god.

10 'I am the Lord your God,
   who brought you up from the land of <u>Egypt</u>; ♦
open your mouth wide and <u>I</u> shall fill it.'

Glory be to the Father and to the <u>Son</u>; ♦
and to the <u>Holy</u> Spirit;
as it was in the beginning is <u>now</u> ♦
and shall be for <u>ever</u>. Amen.

Psalm 82

David Wilson

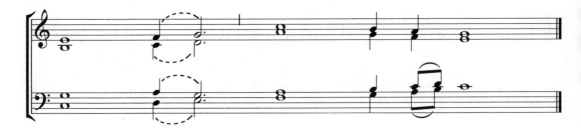

1 God has taken his stand in the council <u>of</u> heaven; ♦
  in the midst of the gods <u>he</u> gives judgement:

2 'How long will you judge un<u>just</u>ly ♦
  and show such favour <u>to</u> the wicked?

3 'You were to judge the weak and the <u>or</u>phan; ♦
  defend the right of the <u>humble</u> and needy;

4 'Rescue the weak and the <u>poor</u>; ♦
  deliver them from the <u>hand of</u> the wicked.

5 'They have no knowledge or wisdom;
    they walk on still in <u>dark</u>ness: ♦
  all the foundations of the <u>earth</u> are shaken.

6 'Therefore I say that though <u>you are</u> gods ♦
  and all of you children <u>of the</u> Most High,

7 'Nevertheless, you shall die <u>like</u> mortals ♦
  and fall like <u>one of</u> their princes.'

8 Arise, O God and judge <u>the</u> earth, ♦
  for it is you that shall take all nations for <u>your</u> possession.

  Glory be to the Father and to the <u>Son</u>; ♦
  and to the <u>Ho</u>ly Spirit;
  as it was in the beginning is <u>now</u> ♦
  and shall be for <u>ever</u>. Amen.

Psalm 84

Noël Tredinnick

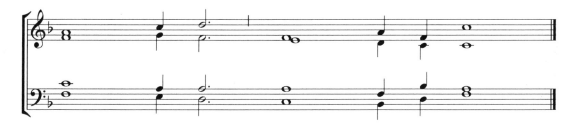

1 How lovely is your dwelling place, O Lord of hosts! ♦
   My soul has a desire and longing to enter the courts of the Lord;
      my heart and my flesh rejoice in the living God.

2 The sparrow has found her a house
      and the swallow a nest where she may lay her young: ♦
   at your altars, O Lord of hosts, my King and my God.

3 Blessed are they who dwell in your house: ♦
   they will always be praising you.

4 Blessed are those whose strength is in you, ♦
   in whose heart are the highways to Zion,

5 Who going through the barren valley find there a spring, ♦
   and the early rains will clothe it with blessing.

6 They will go from strength to strength ♦
   and appear before God in Zion.

7 O Lord God of hosts, hear my prayer; ♦
   listen, O God of Jacob.

8 Behold our defender, O God, ♦
   and look upon the face of your anointed.

9 For one day in your courts ♦
   is better than a thousand.

10 I would rather be a doorkeeper in the house of my God ♦
    than dwell in the tents of ungodliness.

11 For the Lord God is both sun and shield;
       he will give grace and glory; ♦
    no good thing shall the Lord withhold
       from those who walk with integrity.

12 O Lord God of hosts, ♦
    blessed are those who put their trust in you.

    Glory be to the Father and to the Son; ♦
    and to the Holy Spirit;
    as it was in the beginning is now ♦
    and shall be for ever. Amen.

Psalm 85

John Barnard

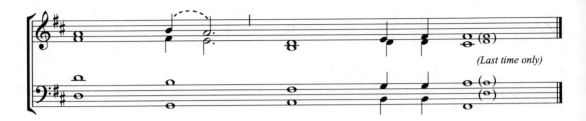

(Last time only)

1 Lord, you were gracious to your <u>land;</u> ♦
you restored the <u>fortunes</u> of Jacob.

2 You forgave the offence of your <u>people</u> ♦
and covered <u>all</u> their sins.

3 You laid aside all your <u>fu</u>-ry ♦
and turned from your wrathful <u>indig</u>nation.

4 Restore us again, O God our <u>Sav</u>iour, ♦
and let your anger <u>cease</u> from us.

5 Will you be displeased with us for <u>ev</u>er? ♦
Will you stretch out your wrath from one generation <u>to</u> another?

6 Will you not give us life <u>a</u>-gain, ♦
that your people may re<u>joice</u> in you?

7 Show us your mercy, O <u>Lord,</u> ♦
and grant us <u>your</u> salvation.

   Glory be to the Father and to the <u>Son;</u> ♦
and to the <u>Ho</u>ly Spirit;
as it was in the beginning is <u>now</u> ♦
and shall be for <u>ev</u>er. Amen.

Psalm 86

Norman Warren

1 Incline your ear, O Lord, and <u>answer</u> me, ♦
   for I am poor <u>and</u> in misery.

2 Preserve my soul, for I am <u>faith</u>ful; ♦
   save your servant, for I put my <u>trust</u> in you.

3 Be merciful to me, O Lord, for you are <u>my</u> God; ♦
   I call upon you <u>all the</u> day long.

4 Gladden the soul of your <u>ser</u>vant, ♦
   for to you, O Lord, I lift <u>up</u> my soul.

5 For you, Lord, are good and forg<u>iv</u>ing, ♦
   abounding in steadfast love to all who <u>call</u> upon you.

6 Give ear, O Lord, to my <u>prayer</u> ♦
   and listen to the voice of my <u>sup</u>plication.

7 In the day of my distress I will <u>call up</u>on you, ♦
   for you will <u>ans</u>wer me.

   Glory be to the Father and to the <u>Son</u>; ♦
   and to the <u>Ho</u>ly Spirit;
   as it was in the beginning is <u>now</u> ♦
   and shall be for <u>ev</u>er. Amen.

Psalm 89

Barry Ferguson

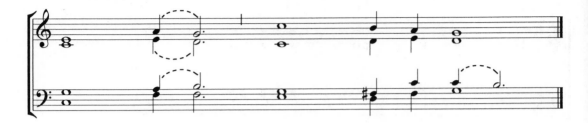

1 My song shall be always of the loving-kindness of the <u>Lord</u>: ♦
   with my mouth will I proclaim your faithfulness
   throughout all <u>ge</u>nerations.

2 I will declare that your love is established for <u>e</u>ver; ♦
   you have set your faithfulness as <u>firm as</u> the heavens.

3 For you said: 'I have made a covenant with my <u>chosen</u> one; ♦
   I have sworn an oath to <u>David</u> my servant:

4 ' "Your seed will I establish for <u>e</u>ver ♦
   and build up your throne for all <u>ge</u>nerations." '

5 The heavens praise your wonders, O <u>Lord</u>, ♦
   and your faithfulness in the assembly of the <u>ho</u>ly ones;

6 For who among the clouds can be compared to the <u>Lord</u>? ♦
   Who is like the Lord among the <u>host</u> of heaven?

7 A God feared in the council of the <u>ho</u>ly ones, ♦
   great and terrible above all those <u>round a</u>-bout him.

8 Who is like you, Lord God of <u>hosts</u>? ♦
   Mighty Lord, your faithfulness is <u>all</u> around you.

52 Blessed be the Lord for ever<u>more</u>. ♦
    Amen and <u>A</u> -men.

Glory be to the Father and to the <u>Son</u>; ♦
and to the <u>Ho</u>ly Spirit;
as it was in the beginning is <u>now</u> ♦
and shall be for <u>ever</u>. Amen.

Psalm 90

Peter White

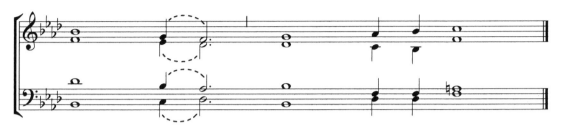

1 Lord, you have been our <u>refuge</u> ♦
 from one generation <u>to</u> another.

2 Before the mountains were brought forth,
  or the earth and the world were <u>formed</u>, ♦
 from everlasting to everlasting <u>you</u> are God.

3 You turn us back to dust and <u>say</u>: ♦
 'Turn back, O <u>children</u> of earth.'

4 For a thousand years in your sight are but as <u>yester</u>day, ♦
 which passes like a <u>watch in</u> the night.

9 When you are angry, all our days are <u>gone</u>; ♦
 our years come to an end <u>like</u> a sigh.

10 The days of our life are three score years and ten,
  or if our strength endures, even <u>four</u> score; ♦
 yet the sum of them is but labour and sorrow,
  for they soon pass away and <u>we</u> are gone.

11 Who regards the power of your <u>wrath</u> ♦
 and your indignation like <u>those</u> who fear you?

12 So teach us to number our <u>days</u> ♦
 that we may apply our <u>hearts</u> to wisdom.

 Glory be to the Father and to the <u>Son</u>; ♦
 and to the <u>Ho</u>ly Spirit;
 as it was in the beginning is <u>now</u> ♦
 and shall be for <u>ever</u>. Amen.

Psalm 91

David Wilson

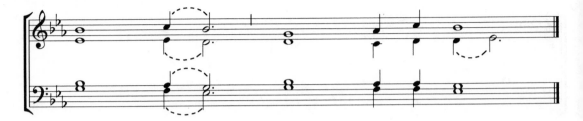

1 Whoever dwells in the shelter of the <u>Most</u> High ♦
   and abides under the shadow of <u>the</u> Almighty,

2 Shall say to the Lord, 'My refuge and my <u>strong</u>hold, ♦
   my God, in whom I <u>put</u> my trust.'

3 For he shall deliver you from the snare of the <u>fowl</u>er ♦
   and from the <u>dead</u>ly pestilence.

4 He shall cover you with his wings
      and you shall be safe under his <u>feath</u>ers; ♦
   his faithfulness shall be your <u>shield</u> and buckler.

5 You shall not be afraid of any terror by <u>night</u>, ♦
   nor of the arrow that <u>flies</u> by day;

7 Though a thousand fall at your side
      and ten thousand at your right <u>hand</u>, ♦
   yet it shall <u>not</u> come near you.

8 Your eyes have only to be<u>hold</u> ♦
   to see the re<u>ward of</u> the wicked.

9 Because you have made the Lord your <u>refuge</u> ♦
   and the Most <u>High</u> your stronghold,

   Glory be to the Father and to the <u>Son</u>; ♦
   and to the <u>Holy</u> Spirit;
   as it was in the beginning is <u>now</u> ♦
   and shall be for <u>ever</u>. Amen.

Psalm 95 *(Venite)*

Norman Warren

1 O come, let us sing to the <u>Lord</u>; ♦
let us heartily rejoice in the rock of <u>our</u> salvation.

2 Let us come into his presence with <u>thanksgiving</u> ♦
and be glad in <u>him</u> with psalms.

3 For the Lord is a great <u>God</u> ♦
and a great king a-<u>bove</u> all gods.

4 In his hand are the depths of the <u>earth</u> ♦
and the heights of the mountains are <u>his</u> also.

5 The sea is his, for he <u>made it</u>, ♦
and his hands have moulded the <u>dry</u> land.

6 Come, let us worship and bow <u>down</u> ♦
and kneel before the <u>Lord</u> our Maker.

7 For he is our <u>God</u>; ♦
we are the people of his pasture and the <u>sheep of</u> his hand.

Glory be to the Father and to the <u>Son</u>; ♦
and to the <u>Holy</u> Spirit;
as it was in the beginning is <u>now</u> ♦
and shall be for <u>ever</u>. Amen.

Psalm 96

Norman Warren

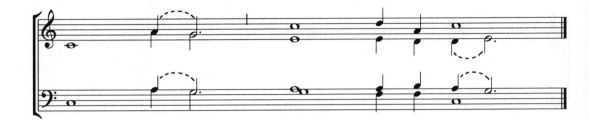

1 Sing to the Lord a new song; ♦
   sing to the Lord, all the earth.

2 Sing to the Lord and bless his name; ♦
   tell out his salvation from day to day.

3 Declare his glory among the nations ♦
   and his wonders among all peoples.

4 For great is the Lord and greatly to be praised; ♦
   he is more to be feared than all gods.

5 For all the gods of the nations are but i-dols; ♦
   it is the Lord who made the heavens.

6 Honour and majesty are before him; ♦
   power and splendour are in his sanctuary.

7 Ascribe to the Lord, you families of the peoples; ♦
   ascribe to the Lord honour and strength.

8 Ascribe to the Lord the honour due to his name; ♦
   bring offerings and come into his courts.

9 O worship the Lord in the beauty of holiness; ♦
   let the whole earth tremble before him.

   Glory be to the Father and to the Son; ♦
   and to the Holy Spirit;
   as it was in the beginning is now ♦
   and shall be for ever. Amen.

Psalm 97

Geoffrey Weaver

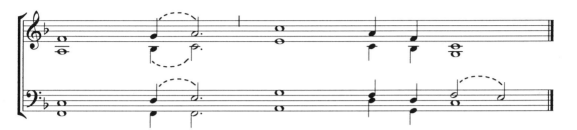

1 The Lord is king: let the earth re-<u>joice</u>; ♦
   let the multitude of the <u>isles</u> be glad.

2 Clouds and darkness are round a-<u>bout</u> him; ♦
   righteousness and justice are the foundation <u>of</u> his throne.

3 Fire goes be-<u>fore</u> him ♦
   and burns up his enemies on <u>every</u> side.

4 His lightnings lit <u>up the</u> world; ♦
   the earth <u>saw it</u> and trembled.

5 The mountains melted like wax at the presence of the <u>Lord</u>, ♦
   at the presence of the Lord of the <u>whole</u> earth.

6 The heavens declared <u>his</u> righteousness, ♦
   and all the peoples have <u>seen</u> his glory.

12 Rejoice in the Lord, you <u>right</u>eous, ♦
   and give thanks to his <u>holy</u> name.

   Glory be to the Father and to the <u>Son</u>; ♦
   and to the <u>Holy</u> Spirit;
   as it was in the beginning is <u>now</u> ♦
   and shall be for <u>ever</u>. Amen.

Psalm 98   *(Cantate Domino)*

Norman Warren

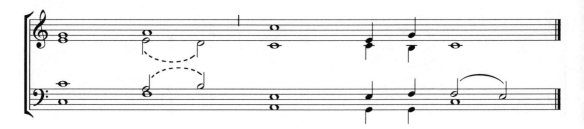

1   Sing to the Lord a new <u>song</u>, ♦
     for he has done <u>marvel</u>lous things.

2   His own right hand and his holy <u>arm</u> ♦
     have won for <u>him</u> the victory.

3   The Lord has made known his sal<u>vation</u>; ♦
     his deliverance has he openly shown in the <u>sight of</u> the nations.

4   He has remembered his mercy and faithfulness
       towards the house of <u>Israel</u>, ♦
     and all the ends of the earth have seen the salvation <u>of</u> our God.

5   Sound praises to the Lord, all the <u>earth</u>; ♦
     break into singing <u>and</u> make music.

6   Make music to the Lord with the <u>lyre</u>, ♦
     with the lyre and the <u>voice</u> of melody.

7   With trumpets and the sound of the <u>horn</u> ♦
     sound praises before the <u>Lord</u>, the King.

     Glory be to the Father and to the <u>Son</u>; ♦
     and to the <u>Holy</u> Spirit;
     as it was in the beginning is <u>now</u> ♦
     and shall be for <u>ever</u>. Amen.

Psalm 99

Barry Ferguson

1 The Lord is king: let the peoples <u>trem</u>ble; ♦
   he is enthroned above the cherubim: let the <u>earth</u> shake.

2 The Lord is great in <u>Zi</u>on ♦
   and high a-<u>bove</u> all peoples.

3 Let them praise your name, which is great and <u>awe</u>some; ♦
   the Lord our <u>God</u> is holy.

4 Mighty king, who loves justice,
      you have established <u>equi</u>ty; ♦
   you have executed justice and <u>righteous</u>ness in Jacob.

5 *Exalt the Lord <u>our</u> God; ♦*
   bow down before his footstool, for <u>he</u> is holy.

6 Moses and Aaron among his priests:
      and Samuel among those who call upon <u>his</u> name; ♦
   they called upon the Lord and he <u>ans</u>wered them.

7 He spoke to them out of the pillar <u>of</u> cloud; ♦
   they kept his testimonies and the <u>law that</u> he gave them.

8 You answered them, O Lord <u>our</u> God; ♦
   you were a God who forgave them
      and pardoned them for <u>their</u> offences.

9 *Exalt the Lord our God*
      and worship him upon his ho<u>ly</u> hill, ♦
   for the Lord our <u>God</u> is holy.

   Glory be to the Father and to the <u>Son</u>; ♦
   and to the <u>Ho</u>ly Spirit;
   as it was in the beginning is <u>now</u> ♦
   and shall be for <u>ever</u>. Amen.

Psalm 100

(Jubilate Deo)

Norman Warren

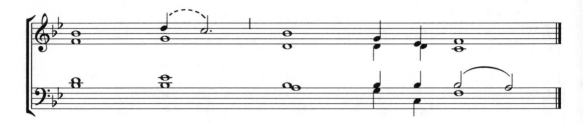

1 O be joyful in the Lord, all the <u>earth</u>; ♦
serve the Lord with gladness
and come before his presence <u>with</u> a song.

2 Know that the Lord is <u>God</u>; ♦
it is he that has made us and we are his;
we are his people and the <u>sheep of</u> his pasture.

3 Enter his gates with thanks<u>giving</u> ♦
and his <u>courts</u> with praise.

4 Give thanks to <u>him</u> ♦
and <u>bless</u> his name.

5 For the Lord is gracious; his steadfast love is ever<u>lasting</u>, ♦
and his faithfulness endures from generation to <u>generation</u>.

Glory be to the Father and to the <u>Son</u>; ♦
and to the <u>Holy</u> Spirit;
as it was in the beginning is <u>now</u> ♦
and shall be for <u>ever</u>. Amen.

Psalm 104

Peter White

1 Bless the Lord, O my soul. ♦
   O Lord my God, how excellent is your greatness!

2 You are clothed with majesty and honour, ♦
   wrapped in light as in a garment.

3 You spread out the heavens like a curtain ♦
   and lay the beams of your dwelling place in the waters above.

4 You make the clouds your chariot ♦
   and ride on the wings of the wind.

5 You make the winds your messengers ♦
   and flames of fire your servants.

6 You laid the foundations of the earth, ♦
   that it never should move at any time.

26 O Lord, how manifold are your works! ♦
   In wisdom you have made them all;
      the earth is full of your creatures.

35 I will sing to the Lord as long as I live; ♦
   I will make music to my God while I have my being.

36 So shall my song please him ♦
   while I rejoice in the Lord.

   Glory be to the Father and to the Son; ♦
   and to the Holy Spirit;
   as it was in the beginning is now ♦
   and shall be for ever. Amen.

Psalm 105

Noël Tredinnick

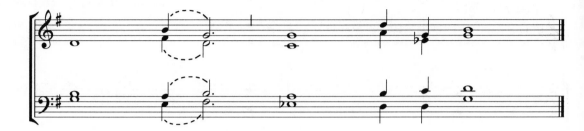

1 O give thanks to the Lord and call upon his <u>name</u>; ♦
make known his deeds a-<u>mong</u> the peoples.

2 Sing to him, sing <u>prai</u>ses, ♦
and tell of all his <u>mar</u>vellous works.

3 Rejoice in the praise of his holy <u>name</u>; ♦
let the hearts of them rejoice who <u>seek</u> the Lord.

4 Seek the Lord and his <u>strength</u>; ♦
seek his <u>face</u> continually.

5 Remember the marvels he has <u>done</u>, ♦
his wonders and the <u>judgements</u> of his mouth,

6 O seed of Abraham his <u>ser</u>vant, ♦
O children of <u>Jacob</u> his chosen.

7 He is the Lord our <u>God</u>; ♦
his judgements are in <u>all</u> the earth.

8 He has always been mindful of his <u>cove</u>nant, ♦
the promise that he made for a <u>thousand</u> generations:

Glory be to the Father and to the <u>Son</u>; ♦
and to the <u>Holy</u> Spirit;
as it was in the beginning is <u>now</u> ♦
and shall be for <u>ever</u>. Amen.

Psalm 106

David Wilson

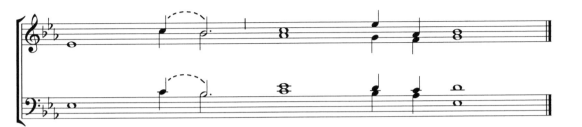

1 Give thanks to the Lord, for he is <u>gra</u>-cious, ♦
for his faithfulness en<u>dures</u> for ever.

2 Who can express the mighty acts of the <u>Lord</u> ♦
or show forth <u>all</u> his praise?

3 Blessed are those who observe what is <u>right</u> ♦
and always do <u>what</u> is just.

4 Remember me, O Lord, in the favour you bear for your <u>people</u>; ♦
visit me in the day of <u>your</u> salvation;

5 That I may see the prosperity of your chosen
and rejoice in the gladness of your <u>people</u>, ♦
and exult with <u>your</u> inheritance.

48 Save us, O Lord our God:
and gather us from among the <u>nations</u>, ♦
that we may give thanks to your holy name:
and glory <u>in</u> your praise.

49 Blessed be the Lord, the God of Israel:
from everlasting and to ever<u>lasting</u>; ♦
and let all the people <u>say</u>, Amen.

Glory be to the Father and to the <u>Son</u>; ♦
and to the <u>Holy</u> Spirit;
as it was in the beginning is <u>now</u> ♦
and shall be for <u>ever</u>. Amen.

Psalm 107

Alan Warren

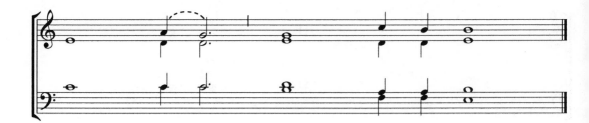

1 O give thanks to the Lord, for he is gra<u>cious</u>, ♦
   for his steadfast love en<u>dures</u> for ever.

2 Let the redeemed of the Lord <u>say</u> this, ♦
   those he redeemed from the <u>hand of</u> the enemy,

3 And gathered out of the lands:
   from the east and from the <u>west</u>, ♦
   from the north and <u>from</u> the south.

4 Some went astray in <u>desert</u> wastes ♦
   and found no path to a <u>city</u> to dwell in.

5 Hungry and <u>thirsty</u>, ♦
   their soul was <u>fainting</u> within them.

6 So they cried to the Lord in their <u>trouble</u> ♦
   and he delivered them from <u>their</u> distress.

7 He set their feet on the right <u>way</u> ♦
   till they came to a <u>city</u> to dwell in.

8 *Let them give thanks to the Lord for his <u>goodness</u> ♦*
   and the wonders he <u>does for</u> his children.

9 *For he satisfies the longing <u>soul</u> ♦*
   and fills the hungry <u>soul</u> with good.

   Glory be to the Father and to the <u>Son</u>; ♦
   and to the <u>Holy</u> Spirit;
   as it was in the beginning is <u>now</u> ♦
   and shall be for <u>ever</u>. Amen.

Psalm 110

Norman Warren

1 The Lord said to my lord, 'Sit at my right hand, ◆
until I make your enemies your footstool.'

2 May the Lord stretch forth the sceptre of your power; ◆
rule from Zion in the midst of your enemies.

3 'Noble are you on this day of your birth; ◆
on the holy mountain, from the womb of the dawn:
  the dew of your new birth is upon you.'

4 The Lord has sworn and will not retract: ◆
'You are a priest for ever after the order of Melchizedek.'

5 The king at your right hand, O Lord, ◆
shall smite down kings in the day of his wrath.

6 In all his majesty, he shall judge among the nations, ◆
smiting heads over all the wide earth.

7 He shall drink from the brook beside the way; ◆
therefore shall he lift high his head.

Glory be to the Father and to the Son; ◆
and to the Holy Spirit;
as it was in the beginning is now ◆
and shall be for ever. Amen.

Psalm 111

Barry Ferguson

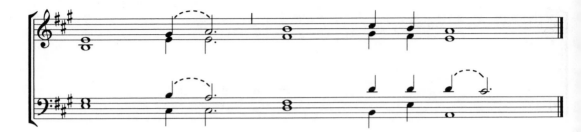

1 I will give thanks to the Lord with my whole <u>heart</u>, ♦
in the company of the faithful and in the <u>congregation</u>.

2 The works of the Lord are <u>great</u>, ♦
sought out by all who de<u>light</u> in them.

3 His work is full of majesty and <u>honour</u> ♦
and his righteousness en<u>dures</u> for ever.

4 He appointed a memorial for his marvellous <u>deeds</u>; ♦
the Lord is gracious and <u>full of</u> compassion.

5 He gave food to those who <u>feared</u> him; ♦
he is ever mindful <u>of</u> his covenant.

6 He showed his people the power of his <u>works</u> ♦
in giving them the heritage <u>of</u> the nations.

7 The works of his hands are truth and <u>justice</u>; ♦
all his com<u>mandments</u> are sure.

8 They stand fast for ever and <u>e</u>-ver; ♦
they are done in <u>truth</u> and equity.

9 He sent redemption to his people;
he commanded his covenant for <u>e</u>-ver; ♦
holy and awesome <u>is</u> his name.

10 The fear of the Lord is the beginning of wisdom;
a good understanding have those who <u>live</u> by it; ♦
his praise en<u>dures</u> for ever.

Glory be to the Father and to the <u>Son</u>; ♦
and to the <u>Holy</u> Spirit;
as it was in the beginning is <u>now</u> ♦
and shall be for <u>ever</u>. Amen.

Psalm 112

Peter White

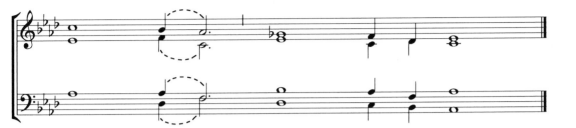

1   Blessed are those who fear the <u>Lord</u> ♦
     and have great delight in <u>his</u> commandments.

2   Their descendants will be mighty in the <u>land</u>, ♦
     a generation of the faithful that <u>will</u> be blest.

3   Wealth and riches will be in their <u>house</u>, ♦
     and their righteousness en<u>dures</u> for ever.

4   Light shines in the darkness for the <u>up</u>right; ♦
     gracious and full of compassion <u>are</u> the righteous.

5   It goes well with those who are generous in <u>lend</u>ing ♦
     and order their af<u>fairs</u> with justice,

6   For they will never be <u>shak</u>en; ♦
     the righteous will be held in ever<u>lasting</u> remembrance.

7   They will not be afraid of any evil <u>tid</u>ings; ♦
     their heart is steadfast, trusting <u>in</u> the Lord.

     Glory be to the Father and to the <u>Son</u>; ♦
     and to the <u>Ho</u>ly Spirit;
     as it was in the beginning is <u>now</u> ♦
     and shall be for <u>ev</u>er. Amen.

Psalm 114

David Wilson

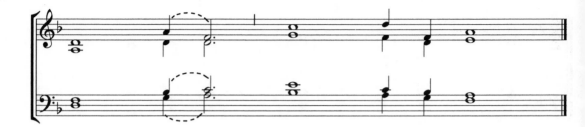

1 When Israel came out of Egypt, ♦
 the house of Jacob from a people of a strange tongue,

2 Judah became his sanctu-ary, ♦
 Israel his dominion.

3 The sea saw that, and fled; ♦
 Jordan was driven back.

4 The mountains skipped like rams, ♦
 the little hills like young sheep.

5 What ailed you, O sea, that you fled? ♦
 O Jordan, that you were driven back?

6 You mountains, that you skipped like rams, ♦
 you little hills like young sheep?

7 Tremble, O earth, at the presence of the Lord, ♦
 at the presence of the God of Jacob,

8 Who turns the hard rock into a pool of water, ♦
 the flint-stone into a springing well.

 Glory be to the Father and to the Son; ♦
 and to the Holy Spirit;
 as it was in the beginning is now ♦
 and shall be for ever. Amen.

Psalm 116

Noël Tredinnick

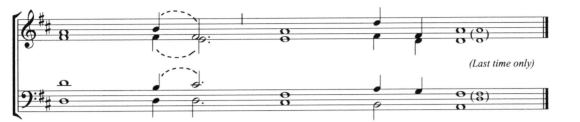

(Last time only)

1 I love the Lord,
for he has heard the voice of my suppli<u>ca</u>tion; ♦
because he inclined his ear to me
on the day I <u>called</u> to him.

2 The snares of death encompassed me;
the pains of hell took <u>hold of</u> me; ♦
by grief and sorrow <u>was</u> I held.

3 Then I called upon the name of the <u>Lord</u>: ♦
'O Lord, I beg you, de<u>liver</u> my soul.'

4 Gracious is the Lord and <u>right</u>eous; ♦
our God is <u>full of</u> compassion.

5 The Lord watches over the <u>sim</u>ple; ♦
I was brought very low and he <u>saved</u> me.

6 Turn again to your rest, O my <u>soul</u>, ♦
for the Lord has been <u>gracious</u> to you.

7 For you have delivered my soul from <u>death</u>, ♦
my eyes from tears and my <u>feet</u> from falling.

8 I will walk before the <u>Lord</u> ♦
in the <u>land of</u> the living.

Glory be to the Father and to the <u>Son</u>; ♦
and to the <u>Holy</u> Spirit;
as it was in the beginning is <u>now</u> ♦
and shall be for <u>ev</u>er. Amen.

Psalm 118

Alan Warren

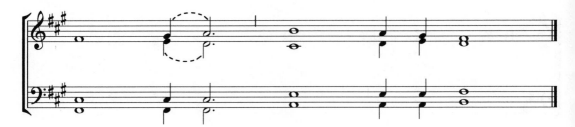

1   O give thanks to the Lord, for he is <u>good</u>; ♦
    his mercy en<u>dures</u> for ever.

2   Let Israel now pro<u>claim</u>, ♦
    'His mercy en<u>dures</u> for ever.'

3   Let the house of Aaron now pro<u>claim</u>, ♦
    'His mercy en<u>dures</u> for ever.'

4   Let those who fear the Lord pro<u>claim</u>, ♦
    'His mercy en<u>dures</u> for ever.'

5   In my constraint I called to the <u>Lord</u>; ♦
    the Lord answered and <u>set</u> me free.

6   The Lord is at my side; I will not <u>fear</u>; ♦
    what can flesh <u>do</u> to me?

7   With the Lord at my side as my <u>sav</u>iour, ♦
    I shall see the downfall <u>of</u> my enemies.

8   It is better to take refuge in the <u>Lord</u> ♦
    than to put any <u>confidence in</u> flesh.

28 You are my God and I will <u>thank</u> you; ♦
    you are my God and <u>I will</u> exalt you.

29 O give thanks to the Lord, for he is <u>good</u>; ♦
    his mercy en<u>dures</u> for ever.

    Glory be to the Father and to the <u>Son</u>; ♦
    and to the <u>Holy</u> Spirit;
    as it was in the beginning is <u>now</u> ♦
    and shall be for <u>ever</u>. Amen.

Psalm 119:1-8

Norman Warren

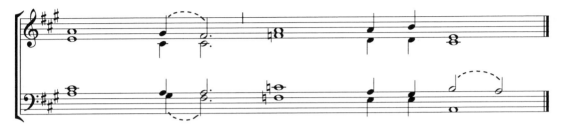

1 Blessed are those whose way is <u>pure</u>, ♦
   who walk in the <u>law of</u> the Lord.

2 Blessed are those who keep his <u>testi</u>-monies ♦
   and seek him with their <u>whole</u> heart,

3 Those who do no <u>wicked</u>ness, ♦
   but <u>walk in</u> his ways.

4 You, O Lord, have <u>charged</u> ♦
   that we should diligently keep <u>your</u> commandments.

5 O that my ways were made so di<u>rect</u> ♦
   that I might <u>keep</u> your statutes.

6 Then should I not be put to <u>shame</u>, ♦
   because I have regard for <u>all your</u> commandments.

7 I will thank you with an unfeigned <u>heart</u> ♦
   when I have learned your <u>right</u>eous judgements.

8 I will keep your <u>statutes</u>; ♦
   O for<u>sake me</u> not utterly.

   Glory be to the Father and to the <u>Son</u>; ♦
   and to the <u>Holy</u> Spirit;
   as it was in the beginning is <u>now</u> ♦
   and shall be for <u>ever</u>. Amen.

Psalm 119:9-16

Barry Ferguson

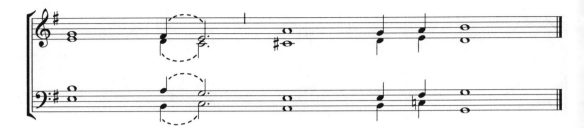

9 How shall young people cleanse <u>their</u> way ♦
  to keep themselves according <u>to</u> your word?

10 With my whole heart have I <u>sought</u> you; ♦
  O let me not go astray from <u>your</u> commandments.

11 Your words have I hidden within <u>my</u> heart, ♦
  that I should not <u>sin a</u>-gainst you.

12 Blessed are you, <u>O</u> Lord; ♦
  O <u>teach me</u> your statutes.

13 With my lips have I <u>been</u> telling ♦
  of all the judgements <u>of</u> your mouth.

14 I have taken greater delight in the way of <u>your</u> testimonies ♦
  than in all <u>manner</u> of riches.

15 I will meditate on your <u>commandments</u> ♦
  and <u>contemplate</u> your ways.

16 My delight shall be in <u>your</u> statutes ♦
  and I will not for<u>get</u> your word.

  Glory be to the Father and to the <u>Son</u>; ♦
  and to the <u>Ho</u>ly Spirit;
  as it was in the beginning is <u>now</u> ♦
  and shall be for <u>ever</u>. Amen.

Psalm 119:33-40

Peter White

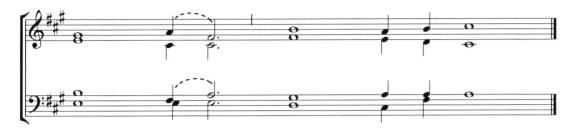

33 Teach me, O Lord, the way of your statutes ♦
   and I shall keep it to the end.

34 Give me understanding and I shall keep your law; ♦
   I shall keep it with my whole heart.

35 Lead me in the path of your commandments, ♦
   for therein is my delight.

36 Incline my heart to your testi-monies ♦
   and not to unjust gain.

37 Turn away my eyes lest they gaze on vanities; ♦
   O give me life in your ways.

38 Confirm to your servant your promise, ♦
   which stands for all who fear you.

39 Turn away the reproach which I dread, ♦
   because your judgements are good.

40 Behold, I long for your commandments; ♦
   in your righteousness give me life.

   Glory be to the Father and to the Son; ♦
   and to the Holy Spirit;
   as it was in the beginning is now ♦
   and shall be for ever. Amen.

Psalm 119:97-104

David Wilson

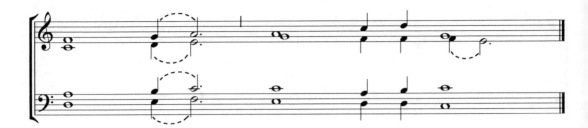

97 Lord, how I love <u>your</u> law! ♦
All the day long it <u>is</u> my study.

98 Your commandments have made me wiser than <u>my</u> enemies, ♦
for they are <u>e</u>-ver with me.

99 I have more understanding than all <u>my</u> teachers, ♦
for your testimonies are my <u>med</u>itation.

100 I am wiser than the <u>ag</u>ed, ♦
because I keep <u>your</u> commandments.

101 I restrain my feet from every <u>evil</u> way, ♦
that I may <u>keep your</u> word.

102 I have not turned aside from <u>your</u> judgements, ♦
for you have <u>been</u> my teacher.

103 How sweet are your words on <u>my</u> tongue! ♦
They are sweeter than honey <u>to</u> my mouth.

104 Through your commandments I get under<u>stand</u>ing; ♦
therefore I hate all <u>ly</u>ing ways.

Glory be to the Father and to the <u>Son</u>; ♦
and to the <u>Ho</u>ly Spirit;
as it was in the beginning is <u>now</u> ♦
and shall be for <u>ever</u>. Amen.

Psalm 119:105-112

Norman Warren

105 Your word is a lantern to my <u>feet</u> ♦
    and a light up<u>on</u> my path.

106 I have sworn and will ful<u>fil</u> it, ♦
    to keep your <u>righ</u>teous judgements.

107 I am troubled above <u>mea</u>sure; ♦
    give me life, O Lord, according <u>to</u> your word.

108 Accept the freewill offering of my mouth, O <u>Lord</u>, ♦
    and <u>teach me</u> your judgements.

109 My soul is ever in my <u>hand</u>, ♦
    yet I do not for<u>get</u> your law.

110 The wicked have laid a <u>snare for</u> me, ♦
    but I have not strayed from <u>your</u> commandments.

111 Your testimonies have I claimed as my heritage for <u>e</u>-ver; ♦
    for they are the very <u>joy of</u> my heart.

112 I have applied my heart to fulfil your <u>statu</u>tes: ♦
    always, <u>even to</u> the end.

    Glory be to the Father and to the <u>Son</u>; ♦
    and to the <u>Holy</u> Spirit;
    as it was in the beginning is <u>now</u> ♦
    and shall be for <u>ever</u>. Amen.

Psalm 119:129-136

Geoffrey Weaver

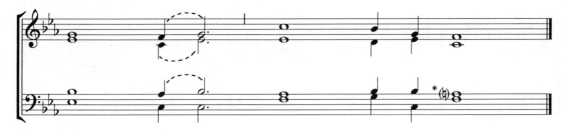

* Tenors sing A♮ last time only.

129 Your testimonies are <u>won</u>derful; ♦
    therefore my <u>soul</u> keeps them.

130 The opening of your word gives <u>light</u>; ♦
    it gives understanding <u>to</u> the simple.

131 I open my mouth and draw in my <u>breath</u>, ♦
    as I long for <u>your</u> commandments.

132 Turn to me and be gracious to <u>me</u>, ♦
    as is your way with those who <u>love</u> your name.

133 Order my steps by your <u>word</u>, ♦
    and let no wickedness have dominion <u>over</u> me.

134 Redeem me from earthly op<u>pre</u>ssors ♦
    so that I may <u>keep your</u> commandments.

135 Show the light of your countenance upon your <u>ser</u>vant ♦
    and <u>teach me</u> your statutes.

136 My eyes run down with streams of <u>wa</u>ter, ♦
    because the wicked do not <u>keep</u> your law.

    Glory be to the Father and to the <u>Son</u>; ♦
    and to the <u>Ho</u>ly Spirit;
    as it was in the beginning is <u>now</u> ♦
    and shall be for <u>ever</u>. Amen.

Psalm 121

Norman Warren

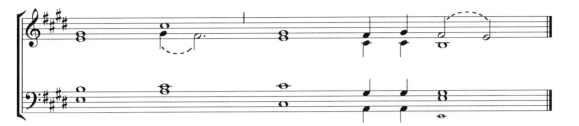

1 I lift up my eyes to the <u>hills</u>; ♦
   from where is my <u>help</u> to come?

2 My help comes from the <u>Lord</u>, ♦
   the maker of <u>heaven</u> and earth.

3 He will not suffer your foot to <u>stumble</u>; ♦
   he who watches over you <u>will</u> not sleep.

4 Behold, he who keeps watch over <u>Israel</u> ♦
   shall neither <u>slumber</u> nor sleep.

5 The Lord himself watches <u>over you</u>; ♦
   the Lord is your shade at <u>your</u> right hand,

6 So that the sun shall not strike you by <u>day</u>, ♦
   neither the <u>moon</u> by night.

7 The Lord shall keep you from all <u>evil</u>; ♦
   it is he who shall <u>keep</u> your soul.

8 The Lord shall keep watch over your going out
      and your coming <u>in</u>, ♦
   from this time forth for <u>evermore</u>.

   Glory be to the Father and to the <u>Son</u>; ♦
   and to the <u>Holy</u> Spirit;
   as it was in the beginning is <u>now</u> ♦
   and shall be for <u>ever</u>. Amen.

Psalm 122

Norman Warren

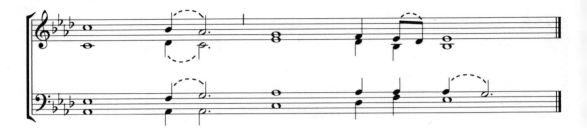

1 I was glad when they said to <u>me</u>, ♦
   'Let us go to the <u>house of</u> the Lord.'

2 And now our feet are <u>stand</u>ing ♦
   within your <u>gates</u>, O Jerusalem;

3 Jerusalem, built as a <u>ci</u>-ty ♦
   that is at unity <u>in</u> itself.

6 O pray for the peace of Jer-<u>usa</u>-lem: ♦
   'May they <u>prosper</u> who love you.

7 'Peace be within your <u>walls</u> ♦
   and tranquillity with<u>in</u> your palaces.'

8 For my kindred and companions' <u>sake</u>, ♦
   I will pray that <u>peace</u> be with you.

9 For the sake of the house of the Lord our <u>God</u>, ♦
   I will seek to <u>do</u> you good.

   Glory be to the Father and to the <u>Son</u>; ♦
   and to the <u>Holy</u> Spirit;
   as it was in the beginning is <u>now</u> ♦
   and shall be for <u>ever</u>. Amen.

Psalm 124

Norman Warren

1 If the Lord himself had not been on our side, ♦
   now may Israel say;

2 If the Lord had not been on our side, ♦
   when enemies rose up against us;

3 Then would they have swallowed us a-live ♦
   when their anger burned against us;

4 Then would the waters have overwhelmed us
     and the torrent gone over our soul; ♦
   over our soul would have swept the ra-ging waters.

5 But blessed be the Lord ♦
   who has not given us over to be a prey for their teeth.

6 Our soul has escaped
     as a bird from the snare of the fowler; ♦
   the snare is broken and we are delivered.

7 Our help is in the name of the Lord, ♦
   who has made heaven and earth.

   Glory be to the Father and to the Son; ♦
   and to the Holy Spirit;
   as it was in the beginning is now ♦
   and shall be for ever. Amen.

Psalm 125

Barry Ferguson

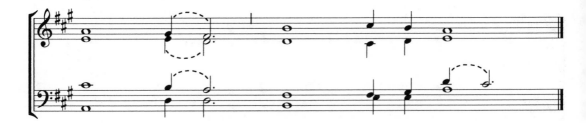

1   Those who trust in the Lord are like Mount <u>Zi</u>on, ◆
    which cannot be moved, but stands <u>fast</u> for ever.

2   As the hills stand about Je<u>ru</u>sa<u>l</u>em, ◆
    so the Lord stands round about his people:
      from this time forth for <u>e</u>vermore.

3   The sceptre of wickedness shall not hold sway:
      over the land allotted to the <u>right</u>eous, ◆
    lest the righteous turn their <u>hands</u> to evil.

4   Do good, O Lord, to those who are <u>good</u>, ◆
    and to those who are <u>true</u> of heart.

5   Those who turn aside to crooked ways:
      the Lord shall take away with the evil<u>do</u>ers; ◆
    but let there be <u>peace up</u>on Israel.

    Glory be to the Father and to the <u>Son</u>; ◆
    and to the <u>Ho</u>ly Spirit;
    as it was in the beginning is <u>now</u> ◆
    and shall be for <u>ev</u>er. Amen.

Psalm 126

Norman Warren

1 When the Lord restored the fortunes of <u>Zi</u>on, ◆
   then were we like <u>those</u> who dream.

2 Then was our mouth filled with <u>laugh</u>ter ◆
   and our tongue with <u>songs</u> of joy.

3 Then said they among the <u>na</u>tions, ◆
   'The Lord has done great <u>things</u> for them.'

4 The Lord has indeed done great things for <u>us</u>, ◆
   and therefore <u>we</u> rejoiced.

5 Restore again our fortunes, O <u>Lord</u>, ◆
   as the river beds <u>of</u> the desert.

6 Those who sow in <u>tears</u> ◆
   shall reap with <u>songs</u> of joy.

7 Those who go out weeping, bearing the <u>seed</u>, ◆
   will come back with shouts of joy:
      bearing their <u>sheaves</u> with them.

   Glory be to the Father and to the <u>Son</u>; ◆
   and to the <u>Ho</u>ly Spirit;
   as it was in the beginning is <u>now</u> ◆
   and shall be for <u>ev</u>er. Amen.

Psalm 127

Norman Warren

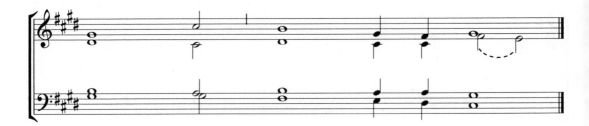

1 Unless the Lord builds the <u>house</u>, ♦
those who build it <u>labour</u> in vain.

2 Unless the Lord keeps the <u>city</u>, ♦
the guard keeps <u>watch</u> in vain.

3 It is in vain that you hasten to rise up early:
and go so late to rest, eating the bread of <u>toil</u>, ♦
for he gives his be<u>lov</u>ed sleep.

4 Children are a heritage from the <u>Lord</u> ♦
and the fruit of the womb <u>is</u> his gift.

5 Like arrows in the hand of a <u>warrior</u>, ♦
so are the children <u>of</u> one's youth.

6 Happy are those who have their quiver <u>full of them</u>: ♦
they shall not be put to shame
when they dispute with their enemies <u>in</u> the gate.

Glory be to the Father and to the <u>Son</u>; ♦
and to the <u>Ho</u>ly Spirit;
as it was in the beginning is <u>now</u> ♦
and shall be for <u>ever</u>. Amen.

Psalm 128

Noël Tredinnick

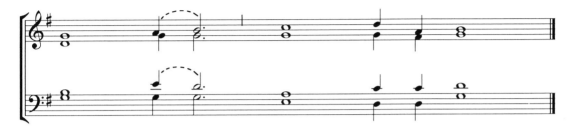

1 Blessed are all those who fear the <u>Lord</u>, ♦
   and <u>walk in</u> his ways.

2 You shall eat the fruit of the toil of your <u>hands</u>; ♦
   it shall go well with you, and <u>happy shall</u> you be.

3 Your wife within your house
      shall be like a <u>fruitful</u> vine; ♦
   your children round your table,
      like fresh <u>o</u>live branches.

4 Thus shall the one <u>be</u> blest ♦
   who <u>fears</u> the Lord.

5 The Lord from out of Zion <u>bless</u> you, ♦
   that you may see Jerusalem in prosperity
      all the <u>days of</u> your life.

6 May you see your children's <u>chil</u>dren, ♦
   and may there be <u>peace up</u>-on Israel.

   Glory be to the Father and to the <u>Son</u>; ♦
   and to the <u>Ho</u>ly Spirit;
   as it was in the beginning is <u>now</u> ♦
   and shall be for <u>ev</u>er. Amen.

Psalm 130

Peter White

(Org. v.1 only)

1   Out of the depths have I cried to you, O Lord:
     Lord, hear my <u>voice</u>; ♦
    let your ears consider well the voice of my <u>sup</u>plication.

2   If you, Lord, were to mark what is done a-<u>miss</u>, ♦
    O Lord, <u>who</u> could stand?

3   But there is forgiveness with <u>you</u>, ♦
    so that you <u>shall</u> be feared.

4   I wait for the Lord; my soul waits for <u>him</u>; ♦
    in his word <u>is</u> my hope.

5   My soul waits for the Lord:
     more than the night watch for the <u>morn</u>ing, ♦
    more than the night watch <u>for</u> the morning.

6   O Israel, wait for the <u>Lord</u>, ♦
    for with the Lord <u>there</u> is mercy;

7   With him is plenteous re<u>demp</u>tion ♦
    and he shall redeem Israel from <u>all</u> their sins.

    Glory be to the Father and to the <u>Son</u>; ♦
    and to the <u>Ho</u>ly Spirit;
    as it was in the beginning is <u>now</u> ♦
    and shall be for <u>ev</u>er. Amen.

Psalm 133

Norman Warren

1 Behold how good and pleasant it is ◆
to dwell together in unity.

2 It is like the precious oil upon the head, ◆
running down upon the beard,

3 Even on Aaron's beard, ◆
running down upon the collar of his clothing.

4 It is like the dew of Hermon ◆
running down upon the hills of Zion.

5 For there the Lord has promised his blessing: ◆
even life for e-vermore.

Glory be to the Father and to the Son; ◆
and to the Holy Spirit;
as it was in the beginning is now ◆
and shall be for ever. Amen.

Psalm 136

David Wilson

1 Give thanks to the Lord, for he is <u>gra</u>cious, ♦
for his mercy en<u>dures</u> for ever.

2 Give thanks to the God <u>of</u> gods, ♦
for his mercy en<u>dures</u> for ever.

3 Give thanks to the Lord <u>of</u> lords, ♦
for his mercy en<u>dures</u> for ever;

4 Who alone does great <u>won</u>ders, ♦
for his mercy en<u>dures</u> for ever;

5 Who by wisdom made the <u>hea</u>vens, ♦
for his mercy en<u>dures</u> for ever;

6 Who laid out the earth upon the <u>wa</u>ters, ♦
for his mercy en<u>dures</u> for ever;

7 Who made the great <u>lights</u>, ♦
for his mercy en<u>dures</u> for ever;

8 The sun to rule <u>the</u> day, ♦
for his mercy en<u>dures</u> for ever;

9 The moon and the stars to govern <u>the</u> night, ♦
for his mercy en<u>dures</u> for ever;

25 Who gives food to all <u>crea</u>tures, ♦
for his mercy en<u>dures</u> for ever.

26 Give thanks to the God <u>of</u> heaven, ♦
for his mercy en<u>dures</u> for ever.

Glory be to the Father and to the <u>Son</u>; ♦
and to the <u>Holy</u> Spirit;
as it was in the beginning is <u>now</u> ♦
and shall be for <u>ever</u>. Amen.

Psalm 137

John Barnard

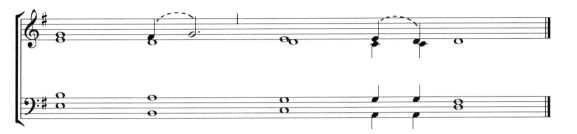

1 By the waters of Babylon we sat down and <u>wept</u>, ♦
 when we re<u>mem</u>bered Zion.

2 As for our lyres, we hung them <u>up</u> ♦
 on the willows that grow <u>in</u> that land.

3 For there our captors asked for a song:
   our tormentors called for <u>mirth</u>: ♦
 'Sing us one of the <u>songs</u> of Zion.'

4 How shall we sing the <u>Lord's</u> song ♦
 in a <u>strange</u> land?

5 If I forget you, O Jer-<u>usa</u>-lem, ♦
 let my right hand for<u>get</u> its skill.

6 Let my tongue cleave to the roof of my mouth:
   if I do not re<u>member</u> you, ♦
 if I set not Jerusalem above my <u>high</u>est joy.

 Glory be to the Father and to the <u>Son</u>; ♦
 and to the <u>Holy</u> Spirit;
 as it was in the beginning is <u>now</u> ♦
 and shall be for <u>ever</u>. Amen.

Psalm 138

Barry Ferguson

This chant may be sung either in Unison or in 4-part Harmony.
The Organ part may be used for either version.

Harmony

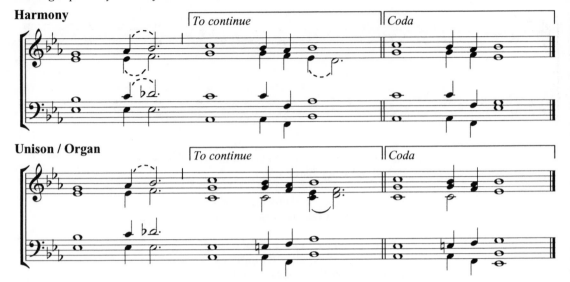

Unison / Organ

1 I will give thanks to you, O Lord, with my <u>whole</u> heart; ♦
   before the gods will I sing <u>praise</u> to you.

2 I will bow down towards your holy temple and praise your name:
       because of your love <u>and</u> faithfulness; ♦
   for you have glorified your name:
       and your <u>word a</u>bove all things.

3 In the day that I called to you, you <u>answered</u> me; ♦
   you put new <u>strength in</u> my soul.

4 All the kings of the earth shall praise you, <u>O</u> Lord, ♦
   for they have heard the <u>words of</u> your mouth.

5 They shall sing of the ways of <u>the</u> Lord, ♦
   that great is the glory <u>of</u> the Lord.

6 Though the Lord be high, he watches over the <u>lowly</u>; ♦
   as for the proud, he regards them <u>from</u> afar.

7 Though I walk in the midst of trouble:
       you will <u>preserve</u> me; ♦
   you will stretch forth your hand against the fury of my enemies:
       your <u>right hand</u> will save me.

8 The Lord shall make good his purpose <u>for</u> me; ♦
   your loving-kindness, O Lord, endures for ever:
   forsake not the <u>work of</u> your hands.

   Glory be to the Father and to the <u>Son</u>; ♦
   and to the <u>Ho</u>ly Spirit;
   as it was in the beginning is <u>now</u> ♦
   and shall be for <u>ever</u>. Amen.

Psalm 139

Norman Warren

1 O Lord, you have searched me out and <u>known</u> me; ♦
 you know my sitting down and my rising up:
  you discern my <u>thoughts from</u> afar.

2 You mark out my journeys and my <u>resting place</u> ♦
 and are acquainted with <u>all</u> my ways.

3 For there is not a word on my <u>tongue</u>, ♦
 but you, O Lord, know it <u>a</u>ltogether.

4 You encompass me behind and be-<u>fore</u> ♦
 and lay your <u>hand</u> upon me.

5 Such knowledge is too <u>wonderful for me</u>, ♦
 so high that I <u>cannot</u> attain it.

23 Search me out, O God, and know my <u>heart</u>; ♦
 try me and ex<u>amine</u> my thoughts.

24 See if there is any way of wickedness <u>in me</u> ♦
 and lead me in the <u>way e</u>-verlasting.

 Glory be to the Father and to the <u>Son</u>; ♦
 and to the <u>Ho</u>ly Spirit;
 as it was in the beginning is <u>now</u> ♦
 and shall be for <u>ever</u>. Amen.

Psalm 146

Peter White

1 Praise the Lord, O my soul:
   while I live will I praise the <u>Lord</u>; ♦
as long as I have any being,
   I will sing praises <u>to</u> my God.

2 Put not your trust in princes,
   nor in any human <u>pow</u>er, ♦
for there is no <u>help</u> in them.

3 When their breath goes forth, they return to the <u>earth</u>; ♦
on that day all their <u>thoughts</u> perish.

4 Happy are those who have the God of Jacob for their <u>help</u>, ♦
whose hope is in the <u>Lord</u> their God;

5 Who made heaven and earth,
   the sea and all that is <u>in</u> them; ♦
who keeps his <u>promise</u> for ever;

6 Who gives justice to those that suffer <u>wrong</u> ♦
and bread to <u>those</u> who hunger.

7 The Lord looses those that are <u>bound</u>; ♦
the Lord opens the <u>eyes of</u> the blind;

8 The Lord lifts up those who are bowed <u>down</u>; ♦
the Lord <u>loves</u> the righteous;

9 The Lord watches over the stranger in the land; ♦
   he upholds the orphan and <u>wid</u>ow; ♦
but the way of the wicked he turns <u>up</u>side down.

10 The Lord shall reign for <u>e</u>-ver, ♦
   your God, O Zion, throughout all generations.
   <u>Al</u>leluia.

   Glory be to the Father and to the <u>Son</u>; ♦
   and to the <u>Ho</u>ly Spirit;
   as it was in the beginning is <u>now</u> ♦
   and shall be for <u>ever</u>. Amen.

Psalm 147

David Wilson

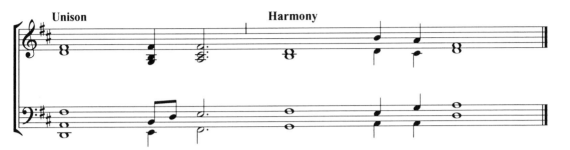

1 How good it is to make music for <u>our</u> God, ♦
   how joyful to <u>honour him</u> with praise.

2 The Lord builds up Jer<u>u</u>salem ♦
   and gathers together the <u>outcasts</u> of Israel.

3 He heals the broken<u>hearted</u> ♦
   and binds up <u>all</u> their wounds.

4 He counts the number of <u>the</u> stars ♦
   and calls them <u>all by</u> their names.

5 Great is our Lord and mighty <u>in</u> power; ♦
   his wisdom is bey<u>ond</u> all telling.

6 The Lord lifts up <u>the</u> poor, ♦
   but casts down the <u>wicked to</u> the ground.

7 Sing to the Lord with <u>thanks</u>giving; ♦
   make music to our God up<u>on</u> the lyre;

   Glory be to the Father and to the <u>Son</u>; ♦
   and to the <u>Ho</u>ly Spirit;
   as it was in the beginning is <u>now</u> ♦
   and shall be for <u>ever</u>. Amen.

Psalm 148

Norman Warren

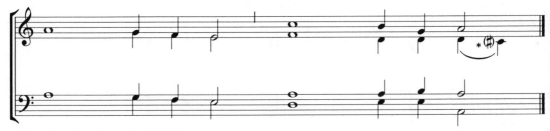

* Altos sing C♯ at the end of the Gloria

1 Praise the <u>Lord from</u> the heavens; ♦
   praise him <u>in</u> the heights.

2 Praise him, all <u>you</u> his angels; ♦
   praise him, <u>all</u> his host.

3 Praise him, <u>sun</u> and moon; ♦
   praise him, all you <u>stars</u> of light.

4 Praise him, <u>heaven</u> of heavens, ♦
   and you waters a-<u>bove</u> the heavens.

5 Let them praise the <u>name of</u> the Lord, ♦
   for he commanded and <u>they were</u> created.

6 He made them fast for <u>ever</u> and ever; ♦
   he gave them a law which shall <u>not pass</u> away.

7 Praise the Lord <u>from</u> the earth, ♦
   you sea monsters <u>and</u> all deeps;

8 Fire and hail, <u>snow</u> and mist, ♦
   tempestuous wind, ful<u>filling</u> his word;

9 Mountains and <u>all</u> hills, ♦
   fruit trees and <u>all</u> cedars;

10 Wild beasts and <u>all</u> cattle, ♦
   creeping things and <u>birds on</u> the wing;

11 Kings of the earth and <u>all</u> peoples, ♦
   princes and all rulers <u>of</u> the world;

12 Young men and women;
   old and <u>young</u> together; ♦
   let them praise the <u>name of</u> the Lord.

   Glory be to the Father and to the <u>Son</u>; ♦
   and to the <u>Ho</u>ly Spirit;
   as it was in the beginning is <u>now</u> ♦
   and shall be for <u>ever</u>. Amen.

Psalm 149

Noël Tredinnick

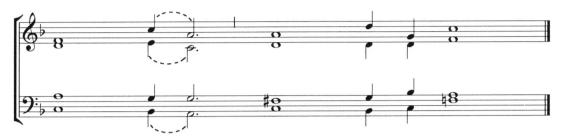

1 O sing to the Lord a new song; ♦
   sing his praise in the congregation of the faithful.

2 Let Israel rejoice in their maker; ♦
   let the children of Zion be joyful in their king.

3 Let them praise his name in the dance; ♦
   let them sing praise to him with timbrel and lyre.

4 For the Lord has pleasure in his people ♦
   and adorns the poor with salvation.

5 Let the faithful be joyful in glory; ♦
   let them rejoice in their ranks,

6 With the praises of God in their mouths ♦
   and a two-edged sword in their hands;

7 To execute vengeance on the na-tions ♦
   and punishment on the peoples;

8 To bind their kings in chains ♦
   and their nobles with fetters of iron;

9 To execute on them the judgement decreed: ♦
   such honour have all his faithful servants.

   Glory be to the Father and to the Son; ♦
   and to the Holy Spirit;
   as it was in the beginning is now ♦
   and shall be for ever. Amen.

Psalm 150

Norman Warren

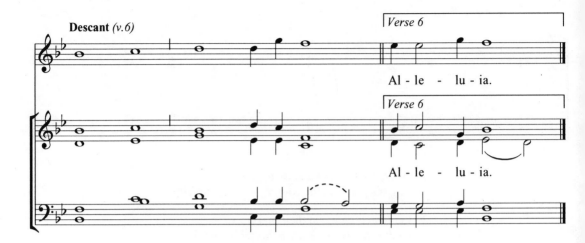

1 O praise God in his <u>holiness</u>; ♦
   praise him in the firmament <u>of</u> his power.

2 Praise him for his mighty <u>acts</u>; ♦
   praise him according to his <u>excel</u>lent greatness.

3 Praise him with the blast of the <u>trumpet</u>; ♦
   praise him upon the <u>harp</u> and lyre.

4 Praise him with timbrel and <u>dances</u>; ♦
   praise him upon the <u>strings</u> and pipe.

5 Praise him with ringing <u>cymbals</u>; ♦
   praise him upon the <u>clash</u>ing cymbals.

6 Let everything that has <u>breath</u> ♦
   <u>praise</u> the Lord.
   Alleluia.

   Glory be to the Father and to the <u>Son</u>; ♦
   and to the <u>Holy</u> Spirit;
   as it was in the beginning is <u>now</u> ♦
   and shall be for <u>ever</u>. Amen.